D1218066

LABORUM
DULCE
LENIMEN
G. SCHIRMER

LUCIA DI LAMMERMOOR

(The Bride of Lammermoor)

Opera in Three Acts

By

G. DONIZETTI

The Italian Libretto Based on
Walter Scott's Novel

The English Version by
NATALIA MACFARREN

With an Essay on the
Story of the Opera by
E. IRENAEUS STEVENSON

Ed. 361

G. SCHIRMER *New York/London*

Lucia di Lammermoor.

A Tragic Drama in Three Acts.

First Performed at the Teatro Fondo, Naples, September 26, 1835. Succeeding First Performances as to other localities included London, 1838; Paris, 1839; New York, in English, at the Park Theatre, 1843, and in Italian, 1849; etc., etc.

Characters of the Drama,

With the Original Cast as Presented at the First Performance.

LORD ENRICO ASHTON . . .	Baritone . .	COSSELLI.
MISS LUCIA, his Sister	Soprano . .	TACCHINARDI-PERSIANI.
SIR EDGARDO DI RAVENSWOOD .	Tenor . .	DUPREZ.
LORD ARTURO BUCKLAW . .	Tenor . .	GIACCHINI.
RAIMONDO BIDEBENT, tutor and confidant of Lucia	Bass . . .	PORTO.
ALISA, companion to Lucia . . .	Mezzo-Soprano	ZAPPUCCI.
NORMANNO, Captain of the Guard at Ravenswood	Tenor . .	ROSSI.

Ladies and Knights related to the Ashtons; Inhabitants of Lammermoor; Pages; Soldiery; and Domestics in the Ashton family.

The action takes place in Scotland, in part in Ravenswood Castle, in part in the ruined tower of Wolfscrag. The time is the close of the Sixteenth Century.

Lucia di Lammermoor.

A just enthusiasm for the novels of Scott was universal when Donizetti, at the height of a brilliant career (to be so tragically shortened), sat down to work into music a libretto sketched by Salvadore Cammerano on the lines of "The Bride of Lammermoor." Every Italian opera-maker of the hour—an hour highly expressive of Italy's lyric drama—burned to set a Walter Scott story to music. The hack-librettist was doing some of his fellest work. Scott was a special favorite of Donizetti's active and decidedly literary mind. He had already produced one "Scott opera" (to-day quite properly forgotten), "Il Castello di Kenilworth," written at about the same time with "Parisina" and "Anna Bolena." With maturer powers, and with the riper art of his "Lucrezia Borgia" (1833), he now began to dress the simple tale of Lucy Ashton and the Master of Ravenswood—as diluted for him by Cammerano. It was, as has been noted, a time of flimsy Italian opera-books. Composers were not fussy. But we know that Donizetti was so little suited with Cammerano's way of making a text for "Lucia," that he re-wrote parts of it, and practically supplied the words and situation for the last act, as he is said to have done for "La Favorita." Let us be kind, and believe that Donizetti improved on Cammerano, and that the French librettists who, in time, revised all the text, improved on Donizetti.

14047

It was not the first time that Scott's touching romance had been turned into opera. But the scores by Donizetti's contemporaries—Carafa (1829), Ricci, by Mazzucato (1834), and Bredal (1832)—are long ago forgotten, with their thin contents. The story of the unhappy Bride, as transcribed by Cammerano and Donizetti himself, is a waterish and feeble report of Scott. It is so familiar that it need not be recited now in detail. We will sketch it briefly. The opera was originally written and given as a two-act work: now it is made a three-act one.

The opera opens in the sombre gardens of Ravenswood Castle, with a group of its guards, and *Normanno*, their head, excitedly talking of discovering whether some stranger is not prowling around the estate on secret mischief. *Lord Enrico Ashton* learns from *Normanno* that the intruder may be no less than *Edgardo di Ravenswood*, their dispossessed enemy. But, worse still, *Normanno* soon adds, in the hearing of the grave *Raimondo* (who, to do him justice, seems not to have guessed it), that *Lucia* is stealing interviews with a mysterious lover, who must be the hated *Edgardo;* and relates the story of *Lucia's* deliverance from a mad bull "while returning from a visit to the grave of her mother." The retainers come in, their errand successful, and describe how a stranger has dashed away from them, on his charger, at the ruined tower. *Enrico* swears vengeance, and the chorus unite in his wish.

The second scene introduces *Lucia*, with *Alisa*, awaiting *Edgardo* in the lonely park, by the haunted spring. *Lucia* has scarcely finished telling its legend of ill-omen, and her own dark dreams of a wretched ending to their secret love-affair, when *Edgardo* enters. He announces that this is a parting; he must leave Scotland that night, on a political errand to France. They discuss—in operatic fashion—their dangers and plans; pledge their mutual faithfulness, and separate in anguish.

With the third tableau, a lapse of some months is supposed to have occurred. The tyrannical *Enrico* has arranged to give *Lucia's* hand to *Arturo Bucklaw*. *Lucia* has not heard from *Edgardo*, the cruel brother having suppressed the lover's letters. She already half-doubts. In a harsh interview, *Enrico* now enjoins the marriage with *Bucklaw*. He produces the usual operatic and dramatic convenience, a forged letter, that makes *Edgardo* faithless to *Lucia*. The unhappy girl is overcome. The guests for the betrothal are already come. A jubilant ceremony begins. The contract is signed by the half-swooning *Lucia*, when *Edgardo* enters. In a tempest of misunderstanding and wounded pride, he denounces *Lucia*, insults her brother and the guests, and quits the apartment with life only through *Raimondo's* good offices in the turbulent scene.

The third act finds *Edgardo* gloomily reflecting, while a storm is crashing around his lonely chamber in the Wolfscrag Tower. But even here *Enrico Ashton* seeks him out with a challenge, and a meeting is arranged. The act's second scene is the wedding of *Lucia* and *Bucklaw*. The festive choruses are broken by *Raimondo's* sudden entrance with the news that *Lucia* is a maniac-bride, and that she has taken her new-made husband's life. The distracted girl comes into the room as *Raimondo* ends his story. She raves—melodiously—and even her brother's anger cannot calm her. As *Lucia* is led away, *Raimondo* rebukes *Normanno* as the tale-teller who has brought all this misery on the Ashtons.

The opera's final scene presents *Edgardo* among the graves of his race. Grief and despair have broken his heart. He is resolved to take his own life. With his last reflections, the sad-hearted Lammermoor folk and some of the Castle guests approach, singing a doleful chant; and a passing-bell is heard. *Raimondo* appears and discloses the fact that *Lucia's* madness has ended in her own death. *Edgardo* apostrophizes her pure spirit, declares that he and she will not long be parted, and stabs himself—dying as the chorus about him piously pray that Heaven may pardon such human errors.

Such is Scott's novel as utilized by Donizetti, in a way amusingly unjust to its own episodes and characters. This operatic *Lucia* has none of that queer mixture of levity, caprice and pride possessing Lucy Ashton, along with all her sentimentality. The *Edgardo* in this libretto is merely a regulation betrayed-lover of the stage, with no touch of Ravenswood's morbid dignity, except where we just catch it in Donizetti's last scene. Our operatic *Arturo Ashton* has few traces of the original Sholto Ashton. And as for the strongest types in "The Bride of Lammermoor," Lord Ashton, the Keeper, Lady Ashton, the impressive figure of Blind Alice (not even caricatured by Cammerano's *Alisa*), old Balderstone the garrulous, and the swaggering Craigengelt—alas, they are left out altogether! We have paper-doll personages, compared with those in the tale. But still there is a general if far-away consonance with it. And it is only fair to remark, in reviewing this typical libretto of the Donizettian, Bellinian, and early-Verdian epoch, that Scott himself slighted opportunities in his book. Donizetti's warbling young lady in her bridal frock does not hint at Scott's poor Lucy Ashton, shuddering in the chimney, raving mad, and hissing out: "So, you've ta'en up your bonny bridegroom!" But Scott failed to make *his* characters act out the bloody tragedy of Lucy's wedding; he merely described it. Perhaps, faithfulness to it, in any way save by a conventional "madness" for *Lucia,* seemed to Donizetti too brutal for the public. It is interesting to speculate what some of the librettists and composer-librettists of our day—Boito, du Locle, Illica—would make of "The Bride of Lammermoor." I suspect that Donizetti's method of disposing of *Edgardo* by a public decease, amid his ancestral tombs, with *Lucia's* funeral train at hand (in which "situation" Donizetti and Wagner's "Tannhäuser" are curiously brought together), would never be encouraged nowadays. We should have *Edgardo* struggling in the "Kelpie" quicksand behind blue gauzes, with a frantic *aria parlante* and very stormy orchestration. I expect, too, that we would begin the opera with the novel's wild bull, and the deliverance of the heroine and Sir Henry. We can hardly keep the bulls out of "Carmen." But, seriously, there is eternally good stuff for a tragic opera in Scott's novel. Be it commended to Puccini or Leoncavallo or Smareglia.

Moreover, while we may smile over the libretto of "Lucia di Lammermoor," it is unfair in these days of Wagnerian and French influences on Italian opera, to treat Donizetti's work with contempt, and to regard it as does one critic of note, who calls it "a sham tragedy"—an "obsolete prima-donna opera." "Lucia di Lammermoor" *is* sentimental; it is wide of the Gluck and Mozart and Beethoven and pre-Wagnerian model, to a fault. But it has musical beauty in lavish measure, and

14047

constant throbs of true dramatic feeling. Its best pages do just what they should do—express the sentimental course of a slight, sad, old-fashioned love-story with a background of romance. There is no hint of local color in its music, but there is not much of that in Scott. There is a poignant sweetness, every now and then, to haunt the ear. Now it is a cavatina like "Regnava nel silenzio," or the grave little introductions to certain scenes, or the passionate sextet "Chi mi frena," or *Edgardo's* "Tu che a Dio" scena, that attests how the composer expressed the spirit of a story as melancholy as the soul of Shakespeare's Jacques. The jigging choruses and thin instrumentation grieve our ears, but there is less conventionality in the latter business, at least, than Donizetti often shows. Wagner writes in 1841, of "La Favorita," that that work of Donizetti, "besides the acknowledged merits of the Italian school," possessed "superior refinement and dignity." The same comment applies to "Lucia"; borrowed from the pen of a master least apt to praise music of such a flavor. The slight, fluent partition is Italian in its casual elegance.

And as to its popularity, "Lucia" seems to be perennial so long as singers really sing. Every leading *soprano di coloratura* studies it and keeps *Lucia* a part in repertory. Every tenor must have *Edgardo's* rôle at command, and his black cloak in wardrobe. To sing *Lucia* perfectly is to be a consummate vocalist. As to deeper qualities, why, if singers will not think of anything but their scales and their shakes, then probably they will not realize with what effect Donizetti's simple recitatives may be delivered. Any such part is a lesson in pure diction.

Indeed, "Lucia di Lammermoor" illustrates Donizetti when serious—not laughing, as when he composes the "Elisire" or "La Figlia del Reggimento," or the equally inimitable "Don Pasquale"—perhaps better than any of his works. It has always divided supremacy with the firmer "La Favorita." It fuses, as does not even "La Favorita," his florid and his dramatic manners. Of all his long list of works—some sixty-seven operas, grave and gay—few survive: really no more than the three humorous masterpieces named and "La Favorita," "Lucia," "Lucrezia Borgia," and "Linda." But they are enough to represent firmly a genius surpassing Bellini, and influencing the early Verdian scores, more directly than generally is understood, and Ponchielli, to say nothing of others. And it is interesting to notice that out of all the endless list of "Walter Scott operas" by composers of almost every nationality to "books" in as many tongues, only "Lucia di Lammermoor" can be considered as keeping the stage, in real repertory to-day; with the exception of Marschner's fine "Templer und Jüdin" (based on "Ivanhoe"), still a favorite in German and Austrian opera-houses. The rival "Lucias" noted above, Carafa's "Prison d'Edimbourg" (on "The Heart of Midlothian"), Bizet's "Jolie Fille de Perth," Balfe's "Il Talismano," and dozens more, are all mute to-day. Sir Arthur Sullivan's recent "Ivanhoe" has not made its way with much vigor or probability of life.

"Lucia" was no heroic score. But it was the outcome of a musical fecundity that we may believe would have achieved higher fruits, but for the cloud of madness—a strange coincidence in the case of a composer who wrote so many "mad-scenes"—coming to Donizetti in Paris, in 1845, and imprisoning him in an asylum until his merciful death in 1848.

E. Irenæus Stevenson.

Index.

ACT I.

(PROLOGUE.)—THE DEPARTURE.

ACT II.

THE MARRIAGE-CONTRACT.

ACT III.

TRADITIONS OF PERFORMANCE

By Estelle Liebling

In Italian opera of this period, it is traditional to use passing and auxiliary notes. Indeed, it was the intention of the composer that they should be used.

PASSING NOTES

In *recitativo* passages, when the interval is a third, followed by two notes of the same pitch, the scalic note between is used instead of going directly to the third. Care should be taken that these notes are in the prevailing tonality. The tonality may have been temporarily changed by means of accidentals. The opportunities to use the passing note are numerous throughout the score. Three examples may suffice.

Page 9. Norman:
Tu sei tur - ba - to!
Henry:
Il sa- i
Page 10. Henry:
mia pro- sap- ia

AUXILIARY NOTES

The auxiliary note is generally used at the end of a phrase, where the two final notes are of the same pitch and may be approached from any interval if attractive to the musical ear. This note is usually better as the scalic note above the final note.

As with passing notes, the tonality must be observed carefully.

CUTS

In performance, certain cuts in this opera have become almost a rule. Those listed below may be designated as authentic, for it is thus that the opera is performed by all leading opera companies.

Page 11. After "Oh detto!" (Bide-the-Bent) in 7th measure, cut to last note in 11th measure, page 12 (Henry) "Io fremo!"

Page 14. The 9th measure may be sung thus:

per- fi - do a

Page 15. In the 2nd measure Norman and Bide-the-Bent are silent. In the two final measures on this page, Henry may sing as follows:

fo - - - ra, fo-ra men rio do - lor,

Page 22. At the end of 8th measure, cut to 8th measure, page 27.

Page 28. Last four bars of baritone solo may be sung thus:

rò spe - gne - rò!

Page 32. The 7th measure is usually sung: 

The aria "Regnava nel silenzio", with its many traditional changes, cadenzas, and variants, is published separately by G. Schirmer, Inc.

Page 36. The following cadenza replaces the 5th and 6th measures.

There is a cut from the end of the 12th measure on page 40, to 1st measure on page 42. Use the word "me" in this latter measure. Alice *tacet* in last 5 measures.

Page 42, No. 4, 1st measure Alice

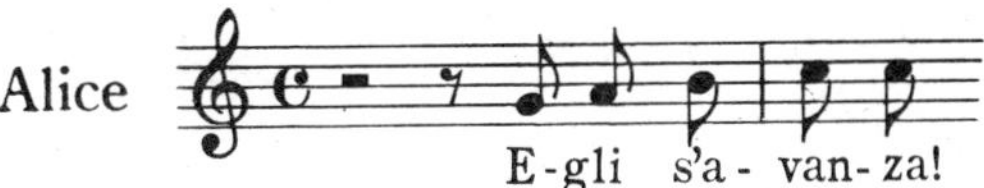

E-gli s'a- van- za!

Page 46, 6th measure Edgar

tre - ma!

Page 46, 23rd measure

trei, ah!

Page 48, 10th measure

Page 49, 5th measure Edgar

Page 55. Measures 20 to 25 for Lucy are silent.

Page 56. The vocal parts in the first 11 measures are silent.

Page 58. The 5th, 6th, and 7th measures are sung in unison by Lucy and Edgar thus:

Edgar thus:
que-sto pe - gno al - lor,

Page 59. Measures 14, 15, 16, 17, and 18 are treated thus:

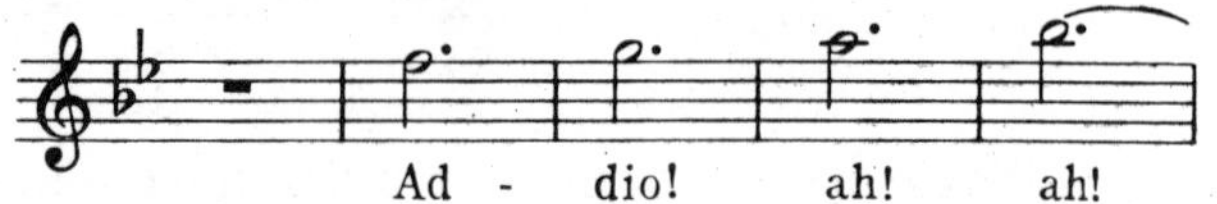
Ad - dio! ah! ah!

and sung by Soprano and Tenor in unison.

Page 65. Cut from end of 2nd measure to beginning of 9th.

Page 65. Cadenza for 12th measure:

do- lor,________ il mio do-lor!

Page 67. Cut from end of 5th measure to beginning of 12th.

Page 70. The 12th measure is sung as follows:

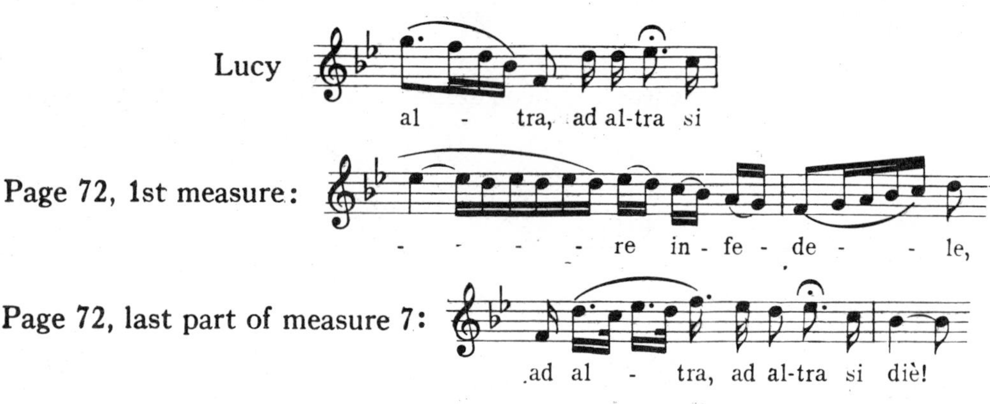
Lucy
al - tra, ad al-tra si
Page 72, 1st measure:
- - - - re in - fe - de - - le,
Page 72, last part of measure 7:
ad al - tra, ad al-tra si diè!

Page 77. The 32nd measure should be sung thus:

ra - ta, ah!__

Then cut to 22nd measure on page 79 (*a tempo*).

Page 80. Cut from the end of the 7th measure to the 2nd measure on page 81.

Page 81. Last two vocal measures:

Lucy
per me.

Then from the end of this page, cut to page 92, No. 8.

Page 122. It is traditional to allow Edgar and Henry to finish their phrases before the others join them in the last 3 measures. The parts of Lucy and Alice are here added to make the explanation clear.

Page 138. Cut from the end of the page to the 5th measure of page 153.

Page 156. Cut to page 173 (No. 11, at beginning of Act III, is omitted).

Page 182, 8th measure. Instead of last beat of measure, the following cadenza is used:

Page 185. From end of 2nd measure, cut to 4th measure (Più mosso) of page 187.

Page 190. "The Mad Scene" is published separately by G. Schirmer, Inc., and includes the well-known cadenzas, etc.

Pages 198 and 199. After the cadenza with Flute at the conclusion of the Mad Scene, Norman, Bide-the-Bent, and Chorus are silent. Cut to 4th measure (Moderato) on page 206.

Pages 208 and 209. The voices of Henry and Bide-the-Bent are omitted.

Page 210, 1st measure:

Measures 7–8:

Measure 9:

Measures 14–16:

Page 211, measures 5–8:

Page 211. Cut from last measure to 8th measure on page 214, thus:

Lucy *tacet* the 7 succeeding measures, and finishes thus:

The last five measures for chorus are omitted.

Lucia di Lammermoor

Lucia di Lammermoor.

Act I.

La Partenza. (The Departure.)

Nº 1. "Percorriamo le spiagge vicine.,,

Prelude and Introductory Chorus.

Scene.– Grounds near the Castle of Ravenswood.

G. DONIZETTI.

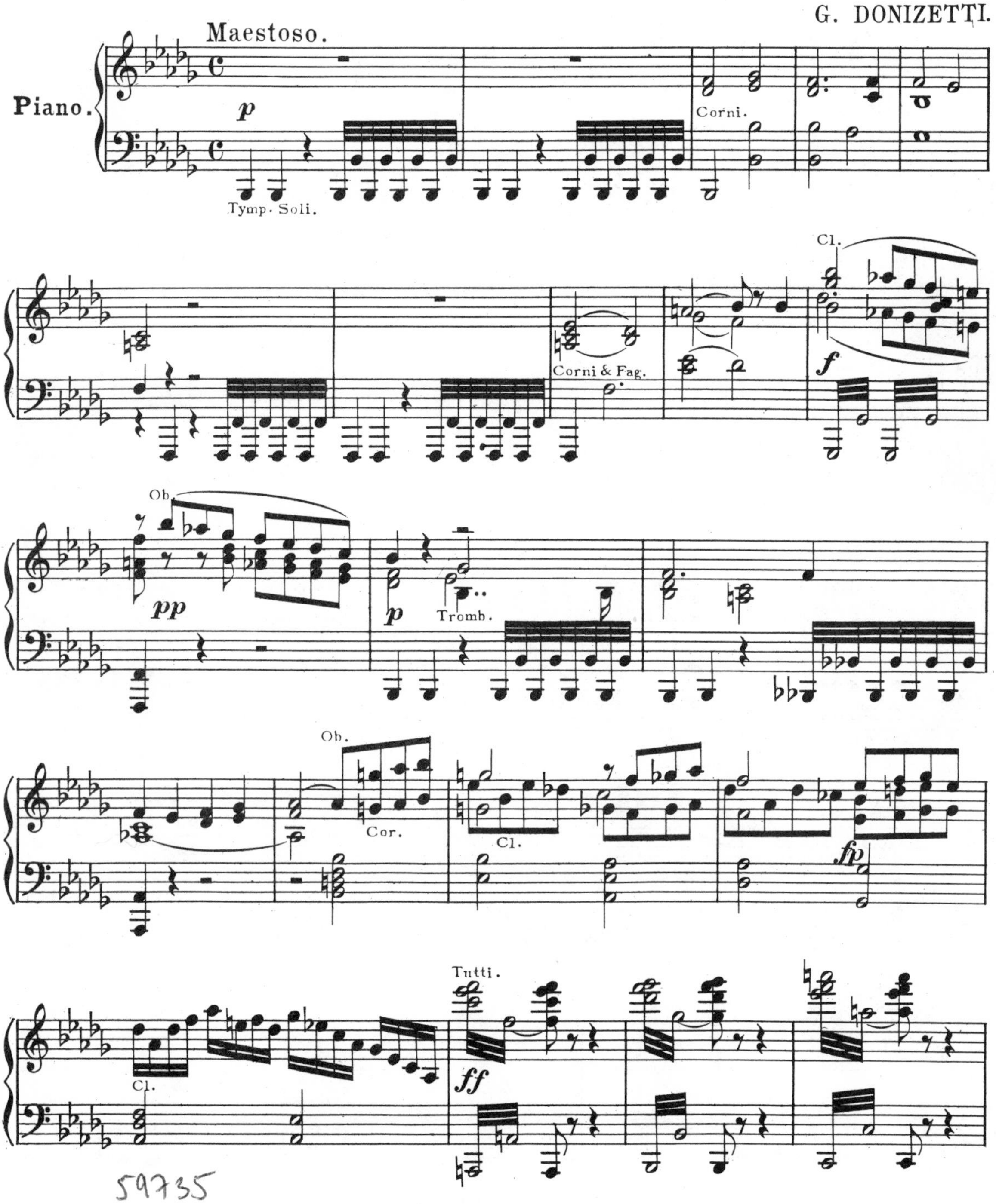

Maestoso.

Piano.

p

Tymp. Soli.

Corni.

Cl.

Corni & Fag.

f

Ob.

pp

p

Tromb.

Ob.

Cor.

Cl.

fp

Cl.

Tutti.

ff

Fl.
Cor.
p
Cl.
Tym. & Tromb.
Strings pizz.
Corni.
calando
ppp
Allegro giusto.
ff
Tutti.
Strings Ob. Cl. & Fag.
Trombones & Strings.
p
fp
fp
calando
Cor.
Cl. Tromb.
Cl. Fl.
Ob.
Vl.
rf
Cor. & Bssn.
f
Viole Cor. Fag. & Cello.
Bassi.

Norman.
Per - cor - re - te le spiag - ge vi - ci - ne,
Let us roam thro' these ru - ins de - serted,
Chorus.
TENORS.
(Sir Henry Ashton's retainers, in hunting-array.)
BASSES.
Percor-ria - mo le spiag - ge vi - ci - ne,
Let us roam thro' these ru - ins de - sert - ed,
Per-cor-ria-mo le spiag - ge vi - ci - ne,
Let us roam thro' these ru - ins de - sert - ed,
Tromb.
Cl. Cor. etc. as before.
del - la tor - re le va - ste ro - vi - ne:
Let no long - er the truth be a - vert - ed,
del - la tor - re le va - ste ro - vi - ne:
Let no long - er the truth be a - vert - ed,
del-la tor - re le va - ste ro - vi - ne:
Let no long - er the truth be a - vert - ed,
ca - da il
Let the
sf
ff

vel di sì tur-pe mi-ste-ro, lo do-man-da, lo impo-ne l'o-nor, lo im-
veil now of doubt rend a-sun-der, And re-veal what to hon-or is due, to
ca-da il vel di sì tur-pe mi-ste-ro,
Let the veil now of doubt rend a-sun-der,
ca-da il vel di sì tur-pe mi-ste-ro,
Let the veil now of doubt rend a-sun-der,
po-ne l'o-nor. Splen-de-
hon-or is due. As a
lo im-po-ne l'o-nor. Splen-de-
To hon-or 'tis due. As a
lo im-po-ne l'o-nor. Splen-de-
To hon-or 'tis due. As a
Tromb.
Viola & Fag.
Vl.
Fag. sustain
Strings.
fp
rà l'e-se-cra-bi-le ve-ro co-me lam-po fra
flash from the cloud af-ter thun-der, We will speak, tho' this
rà l'e-se-cra-bi-le ve-ro co-me lam-po fra
flash from the cloud af-ter thun-der, We will speak, tho' this
rà l'e-se-cra-bi-le ve-ro co-me lam-po fra
flash from the cloud af-ter thun-der, We will speak, tho' this
Cl.
Cor. sustain.
Ob.
fp

nu - bi d'or-ror, splen - de - rà, splen - de -
day we may rue; As a flash, as a
nu - bi d'or-ror, splen - de - rà, splen - de -
day we may rue; As a flash, as a
nu - bi d'or-ror, splen - de - rà,
day we may rue; As a flash,
Vln. II. Viola & Tromb.
Cor.
rà, splen - de - rà l'e-se-cra - bi-le ve-ro
flash, as a flash from the cloud af-ter thun-der,
rà, splen - de - rà l'e-se-cra - bi-le ve-ro
flash, as a flash from the cloud af-ter thun-der,
sì, splen - de - rà l'e-se-cra - bi-le ve-ro
flash, as a flash from the cloud af-ter thun-der,
p
pp
co - me lam - po fra nu - bi d'or-ror, fra nu - bi d'or-
We will speak, tho' this day we may rue, this day we may
co - me lam - po fra nu - bi d'or-ror, fra nu - bi d'or-
We will speak, tho' this day we may rue, this day we may
co - me lam - po fra nu - bi d'or-ror,
We will speak, tho' this day we may rue,
Tutti.

f
ror, Ca-da il vel di sì tur-pe mi-ste-ro, sì,
rue, Let the veil now of doubt rend a-sun-der, Yes,
ror, d'or - ror.
rue, we'll speak.
ror, fra nu - bi d'or-ror. Ca-da il vel
rue, this day we may rue, Let the veil
fra nu - bi d'or-ror. Ca-da il vel
this day we may rue, Let the veil
ff
f
di sì tur-pe mi-ste-ro, lo do-man-da, lo im-po-ne l'o-no-re, sì,
let the veil rend a-sun-der, let the veil now of doubt rend a-sun-der, yes,
di sì tur-pe mi-ste-ro, lo do-man-
now of doubt rend a-sun-der, And re-veal
di sì tur-pe mi-ste-ro, lo do-man-
now of doubt rend a-sun-der, And re-veal
f
lo im-po-ne l'o-nor, ca-da il vel, ca-da il vel,
and re-veal, and re-veal what to hon-or is due,
-da, lo im-po-ne l'o-nor, ca-da il vel, ca-da il vel,
what to hon-or is due, what to hon-or is due,
-da, lo im-po-ne l'o-nor, che l'im-po-ne l'o-
what to hon-or is due, what to hon-or is
f

sì l'im-po-ne, l'im-po- - - ne l'o-
and re-veal what to hon- - - or is

l'im - po - ne l'o-
to hon - or is

nor, l'im - po - ne l'o-
due, to hon - or is

Strings, Cl. & Fag.

ff

nor, ca-da il vel, ca-da il vel, sì, l'im-po-ne, l'im-
due, what to hon-or is due, and re-veal what to

nor, ca-da il vel, ca-da il vel,
due, what to hon-or is due,

nor, chè l'im-po-ne l'o-nor,
due, what to hon-or is due,

f

po- - - ne l'o-nor,
hon- - - or is due,

l'im - po - ne l'o - nor,
to hon - or is due,

l'im - po - ne l'o - nor,
to hon - or is due,

ff

Vlns. Fl. & Cl.

Ca - - da, lo
As a flash from
lo do - man - da, lo im - po - ne l'o - nor, lo do - man - da, lo
And re - veal what to hon - or is due, and re - veal what to
Ca - da, ca - da, lo do - man - da, lo
As a flash, as a flash, and re - veal what to
Viole, Cor. & Fag.
Tutti.
Viole.
Tutti.
Più Allegro.
vuol l'o - nor, l'o -
the cloud, what
vuo - le l'o - nor, lo vuol l'o - nor, l'o -
hon - or is due, we will re - veal, what
vuo - le l'o - nor, lo vuol l'o - nor, l'o -
hon - or is due, we will re - veal, what
Più Allegro.
nor, lo vuol l'o - nor, lo vuol l'o - nor.
is to hon - or due, to hon - or due.
(Exeunt Chorus rapidly.)
nor, lo vuol l'o - nor, lo vuol l'o - nor.
is to hon - or due, to hon - or due.
nor, lo vuol l'o - nor, lo vuol l'o - nor.
is to hon - or due, to hon - or due.

Strings, Cl. Cor. & Fag.
Vln. Fl. Corno.
Fag.
calando
No. 2. "Cruda, funesta smania."
Recitative and Cavatina.
Norman. (respectfully approaching Sir Henry.)
Henry Ashton. (frowning haughtily.)
Voice.
Piano.
Strings.
Tutti.
f p
f
(recit.)
Tu sei tur-ba-to! E n'ho ben donde. Il
Thou art dis-or-der'd! And well I may be! Thou
sa - i: de' miei de - sti - ni im - pal - li - dì la stel - la,
know-est, the an-cient glo-ry hath from our house de - part - ed,
Strings, Corni sustain.
a tempo.
fp
Trombs. & Bassi.
p
In - tan-to Ed - gar - do, quel morta - le ne -
While haugh-ty Ed - gar sees the tem - pest de -
Vln I.
f
p
14047

mi-co di mia pro-sapia, dal-le sue ro-vi-ne er-ge la fron-te bal-dan-
scending, sees we are ru-in'd, in his crumbling towers, lonely and proud, he is in
Recit.
zo - sa, e ri - de! So-lo u-na ma-no raf - fer-mar mi
safe - ty and mocks us! One hand a - lone can now from ru - in
puo-te nel va-cil-lan-te mio po-ter. Lu-ci-a o-sa re-spin-ger quel-la
save me, a-vert our for-tune's to - tal wreck: 'tis Lu-cy; and if she dare to dis-o -
Strings.
Bide-the-Bent. (in a con-
ma-no! Ah! suo-ra non m'è co - le - i! Do-len - te
bey me; Ah! I am no more her broth - er! Oh, have com-
ff Strings, Corni & Fag. sustain.
f
Vln. I. & Bassi.
ciliatory tone.)
ver-gin, che ge-me sull' ur-na re - cen-te di ca-ra ma-dre, al
pas-sion, She yet for her moth-er is mourn-ing in bit-ter sor-row, So
Strings.
Ped.
*
Ped.
14047

ta - la - mo po - tri - a vol-ger lo sguardo? Ri-spettiamo un co - re, che trafit - to dal
soon, how can she think of joy or of mar-riage! Let her tears pro-tect her, for to that gentle
p
Norman. (ironically.)
duol, schi-vo è d'a - mo - re. Schi-vo d'a-mor! Lu-cia d'a-mo-re av-vam-pa.
heart love is a stran-ger. She strange to love? Her heart with love is burn - ing.
f allegro
Henry.
Norman. Moderato assai.
Che fa - vel - li! M'u - di - te: El - la sen già co -
Dost thou tell me Now hear me: Sad - ly one day she
Bide-the-Bent.
(Oh det-to!)
(Oh heaven!)
Moderato assai.
Vln. I.
Vln. II. & Viole.
p
là del par - co nel so - lin - go vi - al do - ve la ma-dre gia - ce se -
rov'd, her moth-er had not long been en - tom'd, thro' lone - ly path-ways dream - i - ly
Cl.
fp
Cl.
pol - ta. Im - pe - tu - o - so to - ro ec - co su lei s'av - ven - ta, quan - do per
wand'ring, When from a neighb'ring thicket t'ward her a boar rush'd wild - ly; She stood af -
Ob.
fp
Cl.
f

Allegro.
l'a-ria rim-bombar si sen-te un col-po, e al suol re-pen-te ca-de la
fright-ed, When a sword came brightly flashing, and in a mo-ment slain was the
Cl.
f
Henry.
Norman.
bel-ve. E chi vi-brò quel col-po? Tal che il suo no-me ri-co-prì d'un
monster. Who struck the blow that kill'd him? He, whom to men-tion, would offend thy
Henry.
Norman.
Henry.
ve-lo. Lu-ci-a for-se? L'a-mò. Dun-que il ri-
presence. And did my sis-ter.– She loves. Since, has she
Norman.
Henry.
Norman.
Henry.
vi-de? Ogn' al-ba– E do-ve? In quel vi-a-le. Io fremo! Nè tu scov-ri-sti il se-dut-
met him? Each morning–And where? In yon-der al-ley. Oh fury! But say, dost know her lover's
Norman.
Maestoso.
So-spetto io n'ho soltanto. E tuo ne-mi-co. Tu lo de-
'Tis on-ly a sus-pi-cion. It is thy foeman; He, whom thou
Allegro.
Bide-the-Bent.
tor? Ah, par-la! (Oh ciel!)
name! Ah, tell me! (Oh heav'n!)
Allegro.
Maestoso.
f
Corni, etc.
fp
fp

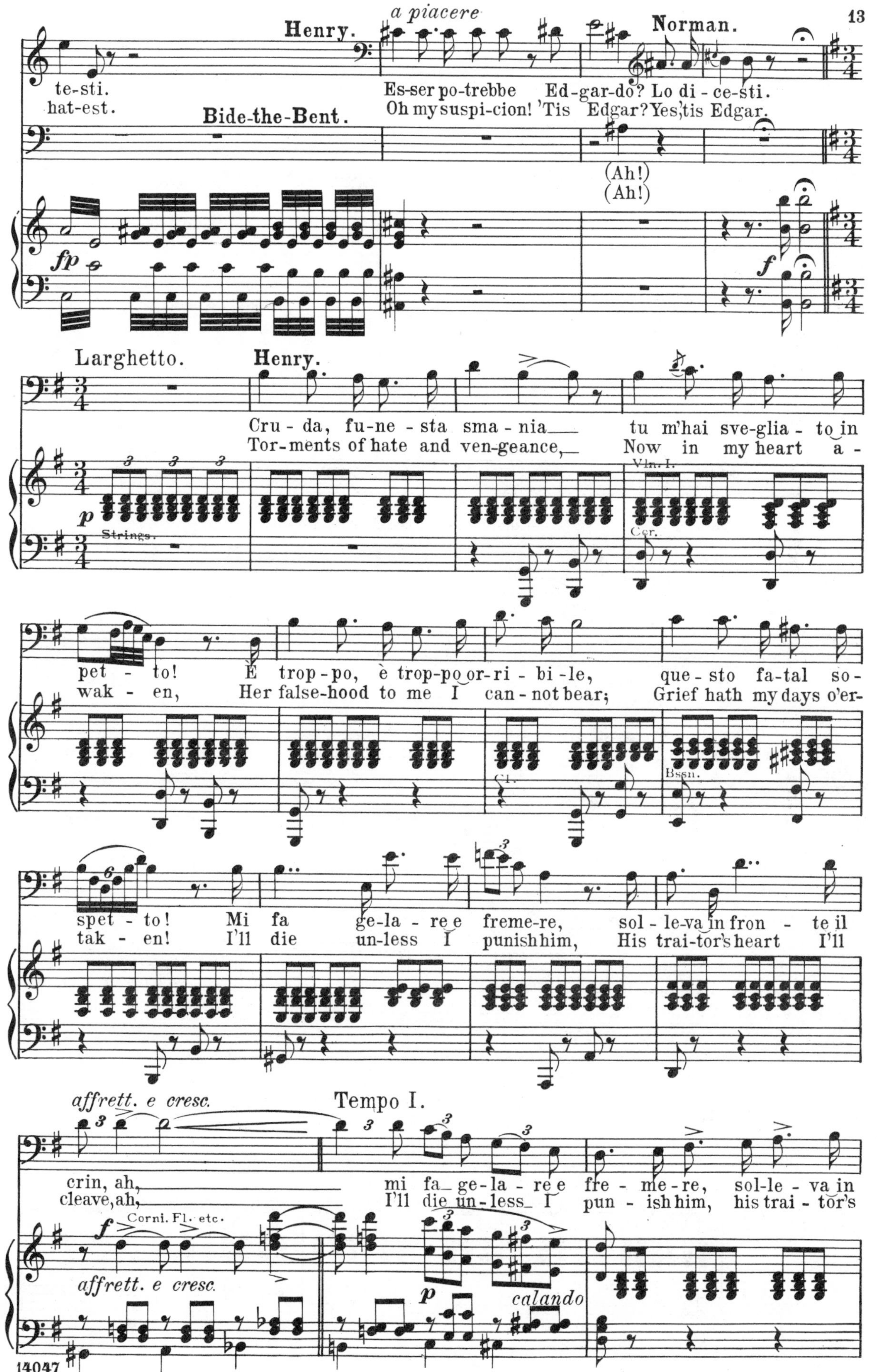
a piacere
Henry.
Norman.
te-sti.
hat-est.
Es-ser po-trebbe Ed-gar-do? Lo di-ce-sti.
Oh my suspi-cion! 'Tis Edgar? Yes, 'tis Edgar.
Bide-the-Bent.
(Ah!)
(Ah!)
fp
f
Larghetto.
Henry.
Cru-da, fu-ne-sta sma-nia tu m'hai sve-glia-to in
Tor-ments of hate and ven-geance, Now in my heart a-
p
Strings.
Vln. I.
Cor.
pet-to! È trop-po, è trop-po or-ri-bi-le, que-sto fa-tal so-
wak-en, Her false-hood to me I can-not bear; Grief hath my days o'er-
Cl.
Bssn.
spet-to! Mi fa ge-la-re e freme-re, sol-le-va in fron-te il
tak-en! I'll die un-less I punish him, His trai-tor's heart I'll
affrett. e cresc.
Tempo I.
crin, ah, mi fa ge-la-re e fre-me-re, sol-le-va in
cleave, ah, I'll die un-less I pun-ish him, his trai-tor's
f
Corni. Fl. etc.
p
calando

fron - te, sol - le - va in fron - te il crin! Col - ma di tan - to ob -
heart, his trai - tor's heart I'll cleave! I from this hour re -
Norman.
p
Pie -
I
Bide-the-Bent.
Tutti.
f
p
bro - brio chi suo - ra a me na - sce - a!
nounce thee, If base - ly thou'st be - tray'd me,
(with a terrible im-
to - so al tuo de - co - ro, io fui con te cru -
spoke to pro - tect thy hon - or, I knew thy heart would
p
(La tua cle - men - za im - plo - ro; tu lo smen - ti - sci, o
(Heav'n, keep thy watch up - on her, Thou wilt not let her
f
pulse of scorn.)
Ah! pria che d'a - mor sì per - fi - do a me sve - lar - ti
Ah! ra - ther than see thee vile - ly wed, Threat'nings and force shall
del.)
grieve.
ciel!)
grieve.)
p stacc.
Fl.

re - a, se ti col-pis-se un ful- - mi - ne, se ti col-pis-se un
aid me, 'Tis to my heart a thun- - der - bolt, 'tis to my heart a
Ciel!
Ah!
Ciel!
Ah!
Tutti.
ff
rall.
a tempo
ful - mi - ne, fo - ra men ri - o, fo - ra men ri-o do-lor, ah!
thun - der-bolt that thou couldst ev - er, that thou couldst ev-er deceive. Ah!
affrett. e cresc.
io fui con
I knew thy
affrett. e cresc.
tu lo smen-
(Thou wilt not
a tempo
p
Fag.
affrett. e cresc.
cresc.
fo - ra men ri - o, fo - ra men ri - o, fo - ra men ri-o do-
that thou couldst ev - er, ev - er de - ceive me, that thou couldst ev-er de-
te, con te cru - del, cru - -
heart, I knew thy heart would
ti - sci, o ciel, ah! o ciel, o
let her, ah no, thou'lt not let her
Tutti.
f

Allegro giusto.
lor.
ceive.
del.
grieve.
del.
grieve.)
Allegro giusto.
Strings, Corni & Fag.
Tutti.
Chorus of Huntsmen. (to Norman)
Il tuo dub-bio è o-mai cer - tez-
Now we know our fear's well found-
Il tuo dub-bio è o-mai cer - tez-
Now we know our fear's well found-
Norman. (to Henry)
Henry.
Andantino.
O - di tu? Nar - ra - te.
Dost thou hear? What mean ye?
za.
ed.
Oh gior - no!
We'll tell thee:
za.
ed.
Oh gior - no!
We'll tell thee:
Andantino.
Bassi pizz.
Strings.
legato
Corni.
Ob. & Fag.
arco

legato
Co - me vin - ti da stan - chez - za, do - po lun - go erra - re in -
Thro' the wood we gai - ly bound - ed, Near yon path - way by the
legato
Co - me vin - ti da stan - chez - za, do - po lun - go erra - re in -
Thro' the wood we gai - ly bound - ed, Near yon path - way by the
legato
p
Cor. & Fag.
Cl.
pizz.
tor - no, noi po - sam - mo del - la tor - re nel ve - sti - bo - lo ca - den - te: ec - co
meadows, There we thought a - while to rest us, Toil and heat had sore op - press'd us; Thro' the
tor - no, noi po - sam - mo del - la tor - re nel ve - sti - bo - lo ca - den - te: ec - co
meadows, There we thought a - while to rest us, Toil and heat had sore op - press'd us; Thro' the
Tutti Strings.
Ob.
to - sto lo tra - scorre in si - len - zio un uom pal - len - te. Co - me appres - so ei n'è ve -
cas - tle's ru - ined gate - way A horse - man pale came rid - ing, Swift - ly, si - lent - ly he
to - sto lo tra - scorre in si - len - zio un uom pal - len - te. Co - me appres - so ei n'è ve -
cas - tle's ru - ined gate - way A horse - man pale came rid - ing, Swift - ly, si - lent - ly he
Cl.
Fag.
nu - to rav - vi - siam lo sco - no - sciu - to: ei su ra - pi - do de - strie - ro s'in - vo -
pass'd us, Not a look or word he cast us, Dark and noise - less as a shad - ow In - to
nu - to rav - vi - siam lo sco - no - sciu - to: ei su ra - pi - do de - strie - ro s'in - vo -
pass'd us, Not a look or word he cast us, Dark and noise - less as a shad - ow In - to
Tutti.
fp

lò dal no- stro sguar- do.
dis - tance soon he fad - ed;
Qual s'ap-
But a
lò dal no- stro sguar- do.
dis- tance soon he fad - ed;
Qual s'ap-
But a
Strings. Fl.
fp
fp
p
p
Cor. & Bassi.
Henry.
E
Who
pel - la unfal- co - nie - ro ne ap - pren - de - va, qual s'ap- pel - la.
huntsman of_ our num-ber knew his name, and hath be - tray'd it.
pel - la unfal- co - nie - ro ne ap - pren - de - va, qual s'ap-pel - la.
huntsman of_ our num-ber knew his name, and hath be - tray'd it.
Cl. Fag. Tym.
Allegro vivace.
qua - le?
is he?
E - gli!_
Ed - gar!
Ed gar- - - -do.
Lord Ed- - - -gar.
Ed - gar- - - -do.
Lord Ed- - - -gar.
Allegro vivace.
f Strings, Brass & Tym.

Oh, rab- -bia, oh! rab- -bia che m'ac-
Oh, ven- -geance, oh! ven- -geance on the
Wood.
Brass.
Wood.
cen- -di, con- -te-
trai- -tor! Doth he
Tutti.
ner- -ti un cor non
dare my wrath de-
può.
fy?
No, con- te-
And doth he
Bide-the-Bent.
Ah, no, non cre-de-re, no, no deh so-
Ah, on her guile-less heart re-ly, She's thy
p
cresc.

ner - ti un cor non può, no, non può, no, non
dare my wrath de - fy? doth he dare, doth he
spen- - - - di_ el - la_
sis- - - - ter_ hear me,
può, no, no!
dare? no, no!
a tempo
U - dir non
a tempo I will not
ah! M'o - di!
ah! Hear me!
a tempo
vo'!
hear!
Strings, Wood & Cor.
ff
Allegro moderato.
f
Viole & Bassi.
Strings, Wood & Cor.
Tutti.
f
f
p

Henry.
La pie-ta- de in suo fa-
If thou plead'st for her, I
Viole & Bassi
Vlns.
vo - re Mi - ti sen - si in-van mi det - ta
scorn thee, Cast thee from me, then let me warn thee,
Fl. & Cl.
Clar.
Tutti.
Cor.
si mi par - li di ven-det - ta so-lo in-ten - der-ti po-
For my wrongs I will have ven-geance, It shall fall on him a-
Cor. & Viola.
Fl.
Fag.
trò. Scia - gu - ra - ti! il mi - o fu - ro - re già su
lone. Wretch-ed sis - ter, thou yet shalt re - pent it! Dost thou
Ob. with voice.
Cor.
'Cello pizz.
Bass pizz.
cresc.
voi tre - men - do rug - ge - l'em - pia fiam - ma che vi
dare to dis - o - bey me? From re - venge now naught can
Tutti.
cresc. Fag.

poco più
strug-ge, io col san-gue spe-gne-rò, io col san- - -
stay me, And his life-blood shall a-tone, and his life- - -
poco più
gue, io col san- gue l'em - pia fiam-ma che vi strug-ge spe-gne-
blood, yes, his life- -blood; naught can stay me, for his life-blood shall a-
cresc.
f
rò, spe- - -gne- -rò, col san - gue spe- gne-
tone, shall a- -tone, his life - blood shall a-
Più mosso
Bide-the-Bent.
rò!
tone! unis.
(Ah! qual
(Ah! what
Ti raf-fre - na, al nuo-vo al- bo - re ei da te fuggir non può, no,
Calm thy wrath, he'll not es - cape thee, With his blood he shall a - tone, he
p
f

nu - be di ter - ro - re.
days are these of griev - ing!
no, non
shall a -
può, ti raf-fre-na, al nuo-vo al-bo - re ei da te fuggir non
tone! Calm thy wrath, he'll not es-cape thee, With his blood he shall a -
cresc.
Henry.
Ta -
Be
que - sta ca - sa cir - con - dò! Ah qual nu - be di ter-
All our an - cient glo - ry flown! Ah! what days are these of
può, no, no, non può. Ti raf - fre - na, al
tone, he shall a - tone, Calm thy wrath, he
ff
f
ce - te, ta - ce - te! Ah!
si - lent, be si - lent. Ah!
ror, ah qual nu - be di ter-ror, sì, que - sta ca - sa cir - con - dò! ah sì!
grief, Ah! what days are these of grief, is all our an - cient glo - ry flown? all flown?
nuo - vo, al nuo - vo al - bo - re ei da te fuggir non può, no, no.
can - not, he can - not es - cape thee, With his blood he shall a - tone, a - tone.
f

Tempo I.
La pie-tà - de in suo fa - vo - re mi - ti sen - si in van mi
If thou plead'st_ for_ her, I scorn thee, Cast thee from me, then let me
Ah!
Ah!
Tempo I.
p
det - ta. Se mi par - li di_ ven-det - ta so - lo in-
warn thee, For my wrongs_ I will have ven-geance, It_ shall
Ah!_ non cre - de - re.
Ah!_ be - lieve it not.
f
p
ten - der - ti_ po - trò. Scia - gu - ra - ti! il mi - o fu-
fall on him a - lone. Wretched sis - ter, thou yet_ shalt re-
Ah!
Ah!
ff
p
ro - re già su voi_ tre - men - do_ rug - ge,
pent_ it! Dost thou dare_ to_ dis - o - bey me?
Qual nu - be di_ ter - ro - re cir - con -
What days_ are these_ of_ grief and sor -
cresc.

l'em-pia fiam - ma che vi strug - ge io — col san - gue spe-gne-
From re - venge — now naught can stay me, And his life - blood shall a-
dò! sì! sì!
row! What days!
Poco più.
rò, io — col san - gue, io — col san - gue l'em - pia fiamma che vi
tone, yes, his life - blood, yes, his life - blood, naught can stay me, for his
Bide - the - Bent.
que - sta ca - sa cir - con - dò! que - sta
All our glo - ry now is flown! all our
E - gli a te fug - gir non può,
With his blood he shall a - tone,
E - gli a te fug - gir non può,
With his blood he shall a - tone,
Poco più.
strug - ge spe - gne - rò, spe - gne - rò, col san - gue spe - gne-
life - blood shall a - tone, shall — a - tone, his life - blood shall a -
ca - sa cir - con - dò, questa ca - sa cir - con - dò, cir - con - dò!
an - cient glo - ry flown, all our an - cient glo - ry flown, all is flown,
no, non può, non puo.
with his blood a - tone.
no, non può, non puo.
with his blood a - tone.

Meno mosso.
Tempo I.
rò, l'em - pia_ fiam - ma che_ vi_ strug - ge, io col san - gue spe - gne -
tone, he_ shall a - tone, he_ shall a - tone, yes, his life - blood shall a -
Tempo I.
Wood
Meno mosso.
Str Vln. sustain
rò, sì, col san - gue
tone! yes, his life - blood
Qual nu - be di ter - ro - re que - sta
What days are these of griev - ing, all our
Ei da te fug -
with his blood he
Ei da te fug -
with his blood he
f
Meno mosso.
spe - gne - rò, l'em - pia_ fiam - ma che_ vi_ strug -
shall a - tone, he_ shall_ a - tone, he_ shall_ a -
ca - sa cir - con - dò, sì, cir - con -
an - cient glo - ry flown, our glo - ry
gir non può, fug - gir non
shall a - tone, he shall a -
gir non può, fug - gir non
shall a - tone, he shall a -
Fl. Cor. Fag.
Meno mosso.

Tempo I.
ge, l'em-pia fiam-ma che vi strug-ge io col san-gue spe-gne-rò, sì,
tone, with his life he shall a - tone, ah, with his life he shall a - tone, he
dò!
flown.
può.
tone.
Str. and Fag.
Tempo I.
cresc.
Tutti.
f
spe - gne - - rò, sì, sì, col san - gue
shall a - - tone, yes with his life he
ah, Que - sta ca - sa
yes, All our an - cient
fug - gir
He shall
spe - gne - rò, sì, spe - gne -
shall a - tone, he shall a -
cir - con - dò, sì, cir - con -
glo - ry's flown, yes, all is
non può, no, no, non
a - - - tone, he shall a -
14047

rò, sì, spe - gne - rò, spe - gne - rò, spe - gne -
tone, he shall a - tone, with his life, with his
dò, sì, cir - con - dò, cir - con - dò, cir - con -
flown, yes, all is flown, all is flown, all is
può, no, no, non può, no, non può, no, non
tone, he shall a - tone, shall a - tone, shall a -
f
p
(Exeunt all.)
ro, col- san- gue- spe - - gne - - - rò!
life, yes, with his life a - - - tone!
dò, sì, que- sta- ca - sa cir - con - dò!
flown, our an - cient glo - ry all is flown!)
può, non può, no, no, no, non può!
tone, yes, with his life shall a - tone!
fff
ff

14047

Nº 3. "Regnava nel silenzio."

Recitative and Cavatina.

The entrance of a park. At the back a practicable gateway; towards the front, a fountain. Lucy Ashton comes out of the Castle, followed by Alice; both are much agitated; they look round, as though seeking some one, and perceiving the fountain, turn away from it.

Cl.
Harp.
cresc.
tr
tr
Harp.
Cor.&Fag.
p
Cor. sustain.
f
Tutti.
Recit.
Lucy Ashton.
An-cor non
Hath he for-
Ob.
Alice.
giunse! In-cau-ta! A che mi trag-gi! Av-ven-tu-rar-ti, or che il fra-tel qui
got me? Im-prudent! To ask him hith-er! Think of thy brother, what if he should dis-
Strings.
pp
Ped.
Ped.

Lucy.
ven-ne, è fol-le ar-dir. Ben par-li! Ed-gar-do
cov-er thou lov'st his foe? I'd warn him! I've call'd him
pp
sappia qual ne cir-con-da or-ri-bi-le pe-ri-glio
Alice.
Per-chè d'in-tor-no il
hith-er that I may tell him what dan-ger lurks a-round him. Ah, where-fore roam thy
Tutti. f
ci-glio vol-gi at-ter-ri-ta?
Lucy.
Quel-la fon-te, ah!
glanc-es wild and af-fright-ed? 'Tis the foun-tain, I
p
ma-i, sen-za tre-mar, non veg-go. Ah, tu lo sa-i: Un Ra-vens-
tremble, when-ev-er I be-hold it. Know'st thou the le-gend? Up-on this
p Strings.
pp
cresc. di forza. a tempo.
wood, ar-den-do di ge-lo-so fu-ror, l'a-ma-ta don-na co-là tra-
spot, they say so, that a Ravens-wood slew the maid that lov'd him, in jeal-ous
cresc. ed incalz.
ff

fis - se, e l'in-fe - li - ce cad - de nel - l'on-da, ed i - vi ri-ma-nea se-
madness! The hapless maid-en rests in its waters, its tide clos'd o - ver her for
lento
Alice.
Lucy.
pol-ta: M'ap-par - ve l'om-bra su - a che di - ci! A -
ev-er. Her wraith once stood be - fore me What say'st thou? I'll
Cor., Tromb. etc.
Larghetto.
scol - ta.
tell thee.
Strings.
Wind & Brass,
Strings.
Re - gna - va nel - si - len - zi - o
In si - lence all lay slum - ber - ing,
Cl. Viola sustain.
al - ta la not - te e bru - na, col - pìa la fon - te un
Dark was the night, and o'er - cloud - ed, No star was gleaming, the
2nd Cl. sustaining.
Cor. Fag.

pal - li - do rag-gio di te - tra lu - na,
pal - lid moon In veils of storm was shroud - ed.
Viole, Cor. & Fag. sustain
quan-do un som-mes - so ge - mi - to fra l'au-re u-dir si
When on the air a sigh was borne, And then a sor - r'wing
Fl.
affrett.
presto
fe', ed ec - co, ec - co su quel mar-gi - ne,
wail, I saw her, on the mar-gin of the tide,
affrett.
f affrett. colla parte
p
(Covering her face with her hands.)
l'om - bra mo-strarsi, l'om - bra mo-strar-si a me, Ah!
There stood a shadow, there stood a shad-ow pale, Ah!
a tempo
Cl.
Strings pizz.
Qual di chi par - la, muo - ver-si il lab-bro su - o ve -
She mov'd her lips as if to speak, But I, a - las, could not

de- - a, e con la ma-no e-sa - ni-me,
hear her, Then, as in warn-ing she wav'd her hand,
chia-mar-mi a sè pa-re- -a;
I did not dare draw near her;
cresc. ed affrett. a poco
stet-te un mo-men - to im-
And while I watch'd her
Vln.
Fl.
Cl.
p
mo- -bi-le, poi rat- -ta di- -le -
mo- -tionless, She van- -ish'd from my
Tutti.
Tempo I.
guò, e l'on-da pria sì lim-pi - da di-
sight, And o'er the stream-let's sil-ver tide Shone
Fl. Cl. with voice.
Harp.
san-gue ros-seg- -giò, sì, pria si lim-pi-da di san-gue ros-seg-
forth a lu-rid light, the streamlet's sil-ver tide shone with a lu-rid
tr
Strings

giò, sì, pria sì lim-pi-da, ah, ___ si ros-seg-
light, there shone a lu-rid light ah, ___ a lu-rid

Allegro. Alice.

giò. Chia- - -ri, ___ oh Di- - -o! ben
light. Pre- - -sage ___ of sor- - -row, that

Vlns.

chia- - -ri ___ e tri- -sti, nel ___ tu- -o
vi- - -sion ___ fore-bod- -ed! Thus ___ do ___ I

dir pre-sa- - -gî ___ in-ten- -do!
fear thy fu- -ture ___ is cloud- -ed!

Ah Lu-ci-a, Lu-ci-a, de-si-sti da un a-mor co-sì tre-
Dear-est Lucy, I pray thee for-go thy fa-tal love, ere grief o'er-

Lucy.
men- -do. E - gli è lu - ce a' giorni mie-i, è con-
whelm thee. Grief dis-solv-eth be-neath his glances, life is
f
f
rall.
for-to, è con-for-to al- mi-o, al mi-o pe- nar.
rapture, life is rapture when he, when he is near.
colla parte
Moderato.
Fl.
Cl.
Strings & Harp.
p
tr
Vln.
Cor. & Fag.
Tutti.
tr
cresc.
f
Strings & Harp.
p
Quan-do ra-pi-to in
Were he but here, oh
Cl.
tr
e - sta-si del più co-cen-te ar-do - re, col fa-vel-lar del
ec - stasy, Naught should I know of sor - row, Bring me a hap-py
Cor.

tr
rall.
p
co - re, mi giu - ra e - ter - na fè, e - ter - na fè,
mor - row, Oh, love, to thee I pray, to thee I pray.
Fl. Cl.
Fl. Ob. Cl.
Tromba.
colla parte
a tempo
in e - sta-si del più co-cen-te ar - do - re,
Oh ec - sta-sy! Naught should I know of sor - row,
col fa-vel-lar del co - re mi giu-ra e-ter-na fè, gli af-
Bring me a hap-py mor - row, Oh, love, to thee I pray. Oh
Vln. Cl. Ob.
fan-ni miei di - men - ti-co, gio-ja di-vie-ne il pian - to,
let my fears be now forgot, One hour of joy, oh grant me,
Cl.
Cor. & Fag. sustain.
par-mi, che a lui d'ac-can - - to si schiu-da il ciel per
Let words of love en - chant me, And trou - ble now flee a -

me, si schiu - da il ciel per
way, and trou - ble now flee a -
Harp.
me, si schiu - da il ciel per
way, yes, flee a -
Poco più mosso.
Alice.
me. Ah! gior - ni d'a - ma - ro
way. May heav'n all thy wish - es
pian - to, ah! s'ap -
grant thee, But, oh,
rinf.
pre - sta - no per te, sì, sì, gior - ni d'a - ma - ro
may'st thou ne'er re - gret this day, heav'n all thy wish - es

pian- -to s'ap - pre- -sta-no per te, per
grant thee, but may'st thou ne'er re-gret, re-
f
te, per te! Ah! Lu-ci-a! ah, de-
gret this day. Dear - est Lu-cy, hear, I
Lucy.
rall.
p a tempo
Ah! Quan-do ra-pi-to in e - sta-si
Ah! Were he but here, oh ec - sta-sy,
si - sti!
pray thee.
p rall.
a tempo
del più co-cen-te ar-do - re, col fa-vel-lar del co-re,
Naught should I know of sor - row, Bring me a hap-py mor - row,
mi giu - ra e-ter-na fè; gli af - fan - ni miei di-
Oh, love, to thee I pray, Oh, let my fears be
p

men- -ti-co, gio-ja di-vie-ne il pian- - - -to,
now for-got, One hour of joy, oh grant me,
par-mi che a lui d'a-can- - -to si schiu-da il ciel per
Let words of love en-chant me, Let trou-ble now flee a-
me, si schiu-da il ciel per
way, let trou-ble now flee a-
me, si schiu-da il ciel per
way, now flee a- - -
Poco più mosso.
me, a lui d'ac-can- -to si
way. One hour of joy, one
p
pp
ff
p
ff

schiu-da il ciel per me, ah!
bright hour of joy grant me, ah!
p
si schiu-da il ciel, il ciel per me, a
let trou-ble flee for e'er a-way; One
f
lui d'ac-can-to si schiu-da il
hour, one hour of joy, one bright hour of
p
ff
p
ciel per me, ah! si schiu-da il
joy grant me, ah! let trou-ble
ciel, il ciel per me, sì, sì, a lui d'ac-can-
flee for e'er a-way, one hour, oh, grant one hour of
Gior-ni d'a-ma-ro
Heav'n all thy wish-es
f sempre

to par si- schiu-da il ciel per me!
joy, grant, oh, grant one hour of joy!
pian - to, sì, s'ap - pre - sta - no per te!
grant thee, may'st thou nev - er rue this day!
Nº 4. "Sulla tomba che rinserra."
Recitative and Duet - Finale I.
Alice.
Voice.
Piano.
E-gli s'a-vanza! La vi-ci-na so-glia io cauta veglie-
I hear him coming, I will stay no longer, but o'er thy safety
Vln.
(re-enters the castle.)
rò.
watch.
Tutti.
Allegro.
Edgar.
Lu-ci-a, per-do-na se ad o-ra i-nu-si-ta-ta io ve-der-ti chie-
For-give me, oh Lu-cy, if at an hour un-wont-ed I have ask'd thee to

de - a: ra-gion pos - sen - te a ciò mi trasse. Pria che in ciel bian-
meet me, but short the moments I yet may tar-ry; when the ear - ly
Str
cheggi l'al-ba no - vel - la, dal - le pa - trie spon - de lun - gi sa -
twi-light brightens to morn-ing, from the shores of Scot-land I shall be
p
Lucy.
Che di-ci!
Oh sorrow!
rò. Pe' fran-chi li-di a-mi-ci sciol-go le ve - le: i - vi trattar m'è
far. Our sails are set to southward, France will re-ceive us, thither I bear a
da-to le sor-ti del-la Scozia.
mission that may re-trieve our country.
Lucy.
E me nel pian-to ab-ban-do-ni co -
And canst thou leave me, for thy ab-sence to
Edgar.
sì? Pria di la-sciar-ti A - sthon mi veg-ga io sten-de-rò pla -
mourn? Ere my de-parture, I'll seek thy brother, There shall be peace be -
fp
f

Che a-
What

cato a lui la destra, e la tua destra, pegno fra noi di pace, chiede-
tween us, strife be forgotten; in pledge of lasting friendship, I then will ask him for thy

fp *p*

Moderato.

(agitated)

scol - - to! Ah no, rimanga nel silenzio se-
say'st thou? ah, no, in silence let our love yet be

rò.
hand.

f *tr*

Moderato. *subito affrett.*

affrett. **Edgar** (ironically) Allegro.

polto per or l'arcano affetto. Inten - do! Di mia
hidden; I know 'twere vain to ask him. Thou know'st him! Him who

Fag. Tromb. and Serpent.

fp Str. *fp* *f*

stirpe il reo persecutor de' mali mie-i ancor pago non
vilely doth persecute my race, whose unjust fury time nor reason can

fp Tromb. *f*

Adagio.
è! Mi tol-se il pa-dre, il mio retag-gio a-vi-to_ Nè ba-sta? Che brama an-
turn! He slew my fa-ther, my her-itage he plunder'd,_ What would he? Is't not e-
Tr.
Tr. sustain.
cor quel cor fe-ro-ce e ri-o? la mia per-di-ta in-te-ra? il sangue
nough? Will but my life-blood suf-fice him, by whose craft I am ruined? E-ternal
Str.
Allegro vivace.
Lucy. Edgar. con forza Lucy.
mi-o? E-gli m'o-dia! Ah no! M'ab-bor-re! Cal-ma, oh ciel, quel-l'i-ra e-
hatred he hath sworn me! Ah no! Oh vengeance! Ah, be calm, thy an-ger
Tutti.
Edgar.
stre-ma! Fiamma ar-den-te in sen mi cor-re!
blinds thee. Fire con-sum-ing with-in me rag-es!
cresc.
Lucy.
M'o-di! Ed-gar-do!
Hear me! Oh Ed-gar!

rall.
M'o - di, e tre - ma!
Hear me, and trem - ble!
Brass.
fp
Larghetto.
Sul - la tomba che rin-ser ra il tra-di - to ge-ni-to-re, al tuo
By the ashes of my fathers, By their tombs, un-wept, unguarded, On thy
Str. pizz.
Horn
(a cry)
Ah!
Ah!
dolce
sangue e-ter - na guerra io giu-rai nel mio fu - ro-re; ma ti
kindred e-ter - nal vengeance I have sworn, my vow's re - corded; But I
cresc.
Cl. Fag. and Tymp.
p Hn.
vi-di, e in cor mi nac-que al - tro af-fet-to, e l'i-ra tac - que. Pur quel
saw thee, my heart re-lent-ed, Thoughts of vengeance I then re-pent-ed, But they
Fl. Cl.
vo - to non è in - fran - to, io po - trei, sì, sì, sì, sì, po - trei compir-lo an-
drive me in - to mad - ness, And that vow, ah yes, that vow I may ful-fil it
p
Fag.
colla voce

Lucy. (con affetto.)
Deh! ti pla - ca, deh! ti pla - ca, deh! ti fre - na!
Calm thy an - ger, calm thy an - ger, turn and heed me,
cor!
yet!
Ah Lu-
Ah!
2d Vln. arco.
Fl. and Cl.
Vln. pizz.
Cor. & Fag. sustain.
Può tra - dir - ne, può tra-dir - ne un so-lo ac-cen - to! Non ti
Though he wrong'd thee, though he wrong'd thee, it was in er - ror! See'st thou
ci - a!
Lu - cy.
ba - sta la mia pe - na? Vuoi ch'io mo - ra di spa-ven-to?
not how I am griev - ing? Wilt thou have me die of ter-ror?
Ah! no, no, no,
Ah! no, no, no,
cresc.
Ce - da, ce - da o - gn'al - tro af - fet - to, so - lo a-
Let not ha - tred, not ha - tred in - spire thee, Let a
no!
no!
f

rall.

mor t'in-fiammi il pet - to; un più no-bi - le, più san - to d'o-gni voto è un puro a-
no - bler passion fire thee, Ah, in happier days I thought thy love for me thou'dst ne'er for-

Pur quel
Yes, they

secondando

rall.

mor, ah, so-lo a - mo - re t'in-fiam-mi il pet - to, ah,
get, ah, once I thought, in hap - pier days, that thy

vo - to non è in-fran - to, io po - tre - i, sì, po -
drive me in - to mad - ness, And that vow, ah, yes, that

cresc. colla parte

a tempo

so - lo, sì, so-lo a-mor, ah, so-lo a - mo - re t'in-fiam - mi il
love thou couldst ne'er for-get, ah once I thought, in hap - pier

tre - i com-pir-lo an-cor, no, non è in-fran - to, io po -
vow, I'll ful-fil it yet, ah, yes, they drive me in - to

a tempo

rall. a tempo

pet - to, ah, so - lo, sì, so-lo a-mor!
days that thy love tho' couldst ne'er for-get!

affrett.

tre - i, sì, po - tre - i com - pir - lo an-cor, io po-
mad - ness, and I may ful-fil it yet, yes, I

arco.

colla parte a tempo p

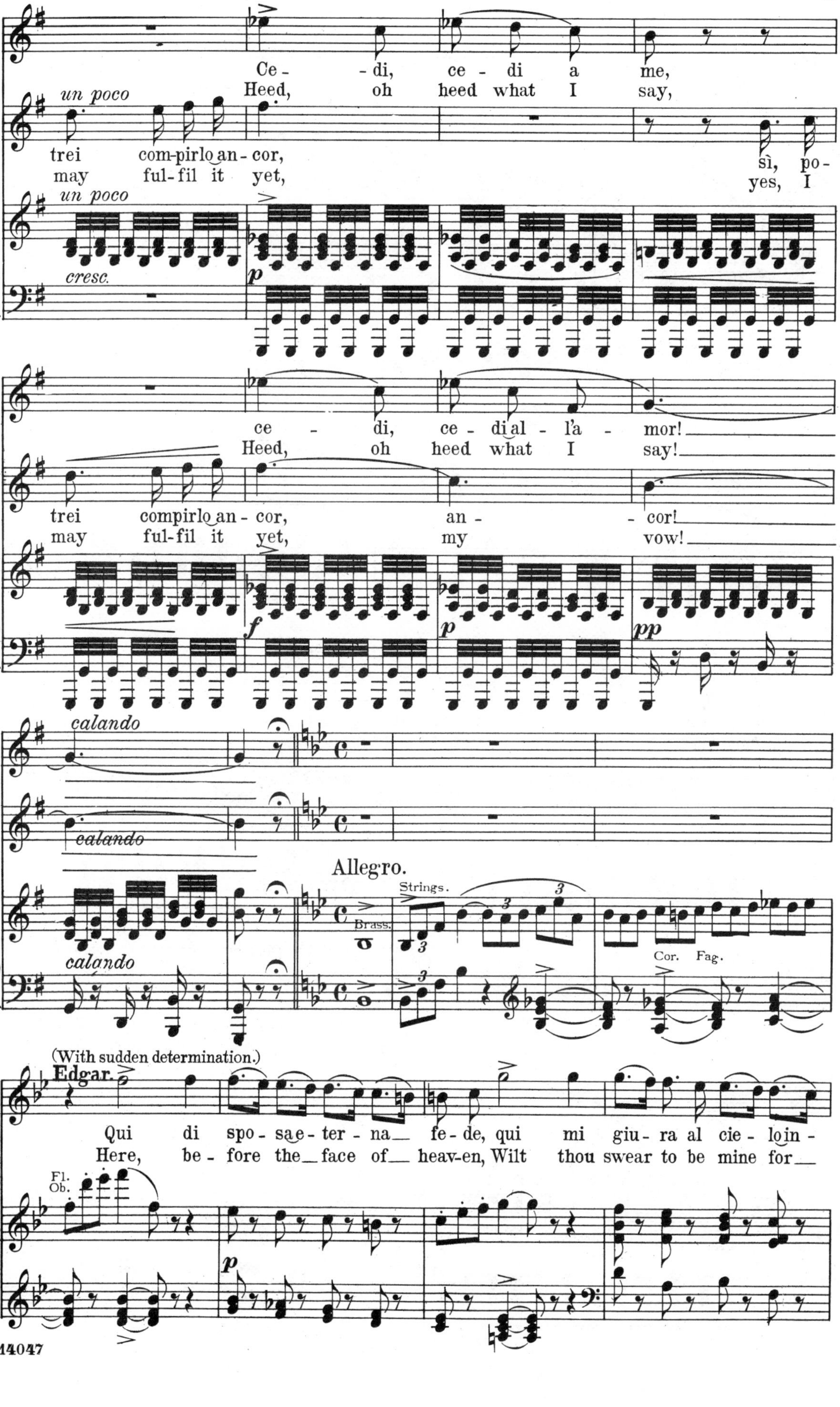

Ce- di, ce- di a me,
Heed, oh heed what I say,
un poco
trei compirlo an-cor, sì, po-
may ful-fil it yet, yes, I
un poco
cresc.
p
ce - di, ce-di al - l'a - mor!
Heed, oh heed what I say!
trei compirlo an-cor, an - cor!
may ful-fil it yet, my vow!
f
p
pp
calando
calando
Allegro.
Strings.
Brass.
calando
Cor. Fag.
(With sudden determination.)
Edgar.
Qui di spo-sa e-ter-na fe-de, qui mi giu-ra al cie-lo in-
Here, be-fore the face of heav-en, Wilt thou swear to be mine for
Fl. Ob.
p

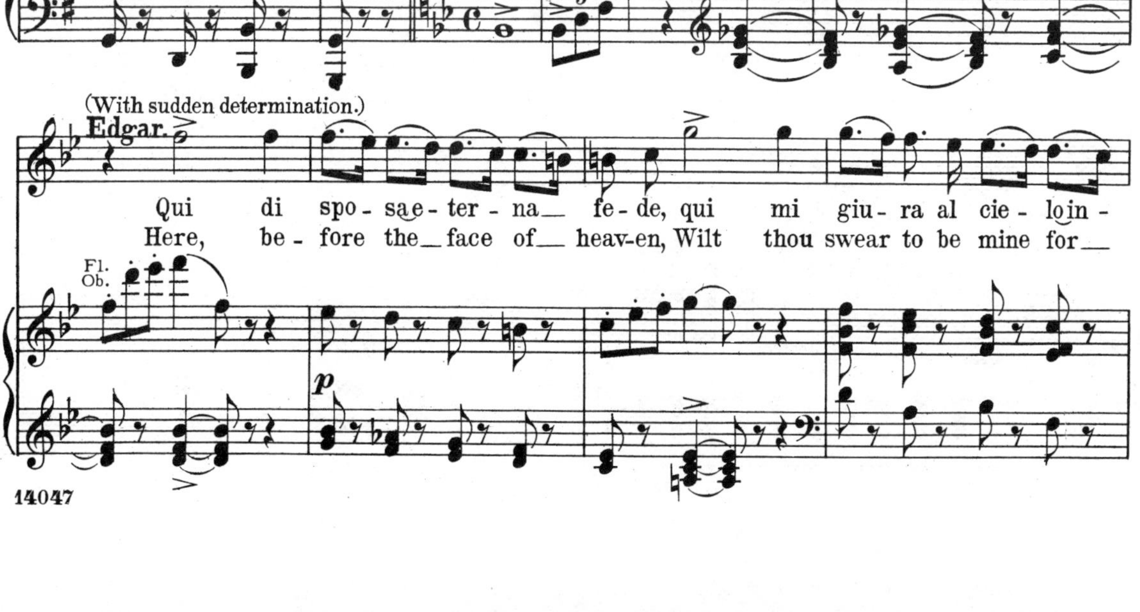

nan - te.
Dio ci a-scol - ta, Dio ci
ev - er?
Spir - its blest are nigh to
Tutti.
f
p
pp
ve - de; tem - pio ed a - ra è un co - re a - man - te;
al tuo
hear us, Say thou'rt mine, tho' we parted for ev - er;
Here I
(putting a ring upon her finger.)
fa - to
u - ni-sco il mi - o:
son tuo
plight thee
my faith e - ter - nal,
Thine for
Lucy. (giving in turn her own ring to Edgar.)
E tua son i - o. Ah! sol-
I'm thine till dy - ing! Ah! the
spo - so.
Ah! sol-
ev - er.
Ah! the

Poco più.
tan - to il no - stro_ fo - co spe - gne - rà di mor - te il gel. A' miei
bliss - ful vow's re - cord - ed, Death a - lone our hearts can di - vide. From all
tan - to il no - stro fo - co spe - gne - rà di mor - te il gel.
bliss - ful vow's re - cord - ed, Death a - lone our hearts can di - vide.
Poco più. Ob. with voices.
Cl.
Cor. Fag. & Tromb. sustain.
p
Violi sustain.
vo - ti a - mo - re in - vo - co, a' miei vo - ti in - vo - co il ciel,
danger, oh be thou guarded, To my pray - er hath heav - en re - plied,
A' miei vo - ti in - vo - co il cie - lo, il ciel, in - vo - co il
From all danger, oh be thou guarded, To my pray'r hath heaven re -
Cl. & Fag.
a' miei vo - ti in - vo - co il cie - lo, in -
From all dan - ger be_ guard - ed for ev - er! ah,
ciel, a' miei vo - ti in - vo - co il ciel, in -
plied, From all dan - ger be_ guard - ed for ev - er,
f
p
ff
vo - co il cie - lo, in - vo - co il ciel.
heav'n_ to my pray - er now hath_ re - plied.
vo - co il ciel, in - vo - co il ciel.
heav - en now to my pray'r_ hath re - plied.
f
p

Oh pa-
Can I
Se - pa - rar - cio - mai con - vie - ne.
For a while I_ now must leave thee.
pp
ro - la a me fu - ne - sta!
live and from thee be part - ed?
f
p
Il mio
Of all
Edgar.
cor - con te - ne - vie - ne. Il mio cor - con te - qui re - sta, il mio
joy_ thou dost be - reave me. Ah, I quit thee bro - ken - heart - ed, Yes, I
f
p
Lucy.
Edgar.
cor con te qui re - sta. Ah! Ed - gar - do! ah! Ed - gar - do! Se - pa -
quit thee bro - ken - heart - ed. Ed - gar, ah, be - lov - ed Ed - gar! Yes, be -
cresc.
fp
Lucy.
a piacere
rar - ci o - mai con - vien.
lov'd one, we must part.
Ah! ta -
Ah! and
col canto

lor del tuo pen-sie-ro ven-ga un fo-glio mes-sag-gie-ro, e la vi-ta fug-gi-
wilt thou send a-to-ken, That thy faith re-mains un-broken, While I sigh for thy re-
Str. pizz. p
Edgar.
ti-va di spe-ran-ze nu-dri-rò. Io di te memo-ria vi-va sempre, o
turning? On that hope my heart shall live. While the flame of life is burn-ing, On thy
Moderato assai.
sempre legato
Lucy.
Ah! Ver-ran-no a te sul-l'a-u-re i
Ah! When twi-light shad-ows low-er, My
ca-ra, ser-be-rò.
mem-'ry I shall live.
Moderato assai.
pp Str pizz.
miei so-spi-ri ar-den-ti, u-drai nel mar che mor-mo-ra,
ar-dent pray'rs as-cend-ing, Will ask that joy on thee may show'r,
Ob. and Hn.
fp
l'e-co de' mie-i la-men-ti. Pen-san-do ch'io di ge-mi-ti mi
Our days of sor-row end-ing. On sighs and pray'rs I now shall live, Un-
Fl.

rinf. f
pa - sco e di do - lor, spar - gi un' a - ma - ra la - gri - ma su
til our part - ing's o'er; Ah, let this to - ken say to thee, I
accel.
que - sto pe - gno al - lor, ah! su que - sto pe - gno al - lor, ah! su
love thee ev - er - more, ah! I love thee ev - er more, ah! I
Fag.
f accel.
Tutti.
f
string.
que - sto pe - gno al - lor, ah! su quel
love thee ev - er - more, I love thee
f 3 string.
Tempo I.
pe - gno al - lor.
ev - er - more!
Ver - ran - no a te sul - l'a - u - re i miei so - spi - ri ar - den -
When twi - light shad - ows low - er, My ar - dent pray'rs as - cend -
Tempo I.
pp
fp
ti, u - drai nel mar che mor - mo - ra l'e - co de' miei la - men -
ing, Will ask that joy on thee may show'r, Our days of sor - row end -

rinf.
ti. Pen - san - do ch'io di ge - mi - ti mi pa - sco e di do - lor,
ing. On sighs and pray'rs I now shall live, Un - til our part - ings o'er,
accel.
spar-gi un' a - ma - ra la - gri - ma su que - sto pe - gno al-lor, ah!
Ah, let this to - ken say to thee, I love thee ev - er-more, ah!
f accel.
Lucy.
string.
Ah! sì, su quel pe - gno al
Ah! I love thee ev - er -
su que-sto pe - gno al-lor, ah! su que-sto pe - gno al
I love thee ev - er-more, ah! I love thee ev - er -
lor, Ed - gar - do
more, my Ed - gar
Poco più mosso.
lor, ah! su quel pe - gno al-lor.
more, I love thee ev - er-more.

Il tuo scrit - to sem - pre vi - va la me - mo - ria in me ter -
While the flame of life is burn - ing, On thy mem - 'ry I shall
Ca - ra!
Dear - est!
f
rà!
live!
p
rall.
Ah! Ver -
Ah! When
Sì, sì, Lu - ci - a, sì, sì.
Ah, dear-est Lu - cy, fare - well!
Fl.
Ob.
rall. pp legato
Cl.
Fag.
Tempo I.
ran - no a me sul - l'a - u - re i tuoi so - spi - ri ar -
twi - light shad - ows low - er, My ar - dent pray'rs as -
Vln. Ob. Cl. with voice.
Harp.
Cor. and Fag. sustain.
Tymp.
den - ti, u - drò nel mar che mor - mo - ra
cend - ing, Will ask that joy on thee may show - er,
fp
Tymp.

l'e - co de' mie - i la - men - ti. Pen - san - do che di
Our days of sor - row end - ing. On sighs and pray'rs I
l'e - co de' mie - i la - men - ti.
Our days of sor - row end - ing.
ge - mi - ti mi pa - sco e di do - lor,
now shall live un - til our part - ing's o'er.
spar - gi su que - sto pe - gno al -
Ah yes, I love thee ev - er -
Edgar.
Spar - gi un' a - ma - ra la - gri - ma su que - sto pe - gno al -
Ah! let this to - ken say to thee, I love thee ev - er -
p
string.
cresc.
lor, ah! su que - sto pe - gno al - lor, ah! su
more, ah! I love thee ev - er - more, ah! I
lor, ah! su que - sto pe - gno al - lor, ah! su
more, ah! I love thee ev - er - more, ah! I
f string.
fp

questo pegno al - lor, ah!
love thee ev - er - more, ah!
questo pegno al - lor, ah!
love thee ev - er - more, ah!
questo pe - gno al - lor,
yes, I love, yes, I love
Più Allegro.
questo pe - gno al - lor,
yes, I love, yes, I love
Più Allegro.
sì, sì, al - lor, sì,
thee ev - er - more, yes,
sì, sì, al - lor, sì,
thee ev - er - more, yes,
sì, al - lor!
ev - er - more!
sì, al - lor! Io par -
ev - er - more! Fare - well

Lucy.
to. Ad - di - o.
then. Ah, fare - well.
Edgar. rall. non tanto
a tempo
Ram - men - ta - ti, ne strin - ge il Ciel!
Re - mem - ber me, thoust plight - ed thy faith!
colla parte
(Lucy retires into the castle.)
Ed - gar - do!
I am thine.
(Exit Edgar.)
Ad - di - o!
Ah, fare - well!
f
End of Act I.

Act II.

Il Contratto nuziale. (The Marriage-contract.)

Nº 5. "Lucia fra poco a te verrà.,,

A fe-steg-giar le noz-ze il-
With pomp to cel-e-brate the

p *p*

lu-stri, già nel ca-stel-lo i no-bi-li pa-ren-ti giunser di mia fa-mi-glia; in
nuptial, I've bidden hither our friends and noble kinsmen; du-ly let them be welcom'd. Sir

(rising in extreme agitation.)

Norman.

breve Artu-ro qui vol-ge. E s'el-la per-ti-na-ce o-sas-se d'oppor-si? Non te-
Arthur, too, will come shortly. But what if she be stubborn, and dare to re-sist me? Fear it

mer: la lun-ga as-sen-za del tuo ne-mi-co, i fo-gli da noi ra-
not. Con-tin-ued ab-sence will have es-trang'd her, the let-ters we in-ter-

fp

pi-ti, e la bu-giar-da nuo-va ch'e-gli s'ac-ce-se d'al-tra
cept-ed, and the re-port sent fly-ing that he an-oth-er bride hath

fiam-ma, in co-re di Lu-ci-a spe-gne-ran-no il cie-co a-
chos-en, will rouse her to re-sent-ment, And to cast off her fool-ish

f

Henry.
mo - re. El - la s'a - van - za. Il si - mu - la - to fo - glio por - gi - mi.
pas - sion. See, where she com - eth. Where's the pretend - ed let - ter? give it me!
f
p
(Norman gives him a letter.)
Ed e - sci sul - la via che tragge al - la cit - tà re - gi - na di Scozia, e qui fra
And now to horse, upon the highway that doth lead to our King's royal cit - y, Proceed un -
f
Allegro.
(Exit Norman.)
plau - si e lie - te gri - da con - duci Ar - tu - ro.
til thou meetest Arthur, and bid him hither.
f
Nº 6. "Il pallor funesto, orrendo."
Recitative and Duet.
Larghetto. Lucy Ashton enters and stands near the doorway.
Recit. Henry.
Henry.
Piano.
Ob.
p
Ap -
Draw
(Lucy Ashton comes forward listlessly, looking fixedly at her brother.)
pres - sa - ti, Lu - ci - a.
near to me, oh, sis - ter!
a tempo

Spe - rai più lie - ta in que-sto dì ve-
With looks more joy-ful this day I thought to

der - ti, in que-sto dì, che d'I - me-neo le fa - ci s'ac-cen - do - no per
find thee, up-on the morn when love and all its bliss-es in-vite thy heart to

Larghetto.

te. Mi guar - di, e ta - ci?
joy. My sis - ter, why si - lent?

Cl.

Moderato.

ff

Lucy.

Il pal-
If my

lor fu-ne - sto, or-ren - do, che ri - co-pre il vol - to mi - o,
cheek is blanch'd with ter - ror, Well thou knowest my cause of griev - ing;

p

ff

ti rim-pro - ve-ro ta-
Ah, re-nounce thy fa-tal
Vln.
pp
cen - do il mio stra - zio,
er - ror, See my weep - ing,
il mio do-lo - re. Per - do -
let me im-plore thee. Mine are
na - re ti pos - sa Id-di - o l'i - nu-
sor - rows past all re - liev - ing, Heav'n for-
cresc.
ma - no tuo ri - gor, per-do-nar-ti pos - sa Id-
give thy harsh re - solve; Mine are sor-rows past all re-
ff

Ce- - di, ce - di a me,
Heed, oh heed what I say,

un poco

trei com-pirlo an-cor, sì, po-
may ful-fil it yet, yes, I

un poco

cresc.

p

ce - di, ce - di al - l'a - mor!
Heed, oh heed what I say!

trei compirlo an - cor, an - - cor!
may ful-fil it yet, my vow!

f *p* *pp*

calando

calando

Allegro.

Strings. Brass.

Cor. Fag.

calando

(With sudden determination.)

Edgar.

Qui di spo - sa e - ter - na - fe - de, qui mi giu - ra al cie - lo in -
Here, be - fore the face of heav-en, Wilt thou swear to be mine for

Fl. Ob.

p

nan - te. Dio ci a-scol - ta, Dio ci
ev - er? Spir - its blest are nigh to

Tutti. *f* *p* *pp*

ve-de; tem-pio ed a - ra è un co-re a-man-te; al tuo
hear us, Say thou'rt mine, tho' we parted for ev-er; Here I

f

(putting a ring upon her finger.)

fa - to u - ni-sco il mi - o: son tuo
plight thee my faith e - ter - nal, Thine for

p *f*

Lucy. (giving in turn her own ring to Edgar.)

E tua son i - o. Ah! sol-
I'm thine till dy - ing! Ah! the

spo - so. Ah! sol-
ev - er. Ah! the

f

Poco più.
tan - to il no - stro_ fo - co spe - gne - rà di mor - te il gel. A' miei
bliss - ful vow's re - cord - ed, Death a - lone our hearts can di - vide. From all
tan - to il no - stro fo - co spe - gne - rà di mor - te il gel.
bliss - ful vow's re - cord - ed, Death a - lone our hearts can di - vide.
Poco più. Ob. with voices. Cl. Cor. Fag. & Tromb. sustain.
p Violi sustain.
vo - ti a - mo - re in - vo - co, a' miei vo - ti in - vo - co il ciel,
danger, oh be thou guarded, To my pray - er hath heav - en re - plied,
A' miei vo - ti in - vo - co il cie - lo, il ciel, in - vo - co il
From all danger, oh be thou guarded, To my pray'r hath heaven re -
Cl. & Fag.
a' miei vo - ti in - vo - co il cie - lo, in -
From all dan - ger be guard - ed for ev - er! ah,
ciel, a' miei vo - ti in - vo - co il ciel, in -
plied, From all dan - ger be guard - ed for ev - er,
f p ff
vo - co il cie - lo, in - vo - co il ciel.
heav'n to my pray - er now hath re - plied.
vo - co il ciel, in - vo - co il ciel.
heav - en now to my pray'r hath re - plied.
f p

Oh pa-
Can I
Se - pa - rar - ci o - mai con - vie - ne.
For a while I now must leave thee.
pp
ro - la a me fu - ne - sta!
live and from thee be part - ed?
Il mio
Of all
f
p
Edgar.
cor - con te - ne - vie - ne. Il mio cor - con te - qui re - sta, il mio
joy thou dost be - reave me. Ah, I quit thee bro - ken - heart - ed, Yes, I
f
p
f
Lucy.
Edgar.
cor con te qui re - sta. Ah! Ed - gar - do! ah! Ed - gar - do! Se - pa -
quit thee bro - ken - heart - ed. Ed - gar, ah, be - lov - ed Ed - gar! Yes, be -
cresc.
f
fp
Lucy.
a piacere
rar - ci o - mai con - vien.
lov'd one, we must part.
Ah! ta -
Ah! and
col canto

lor del tuo pen-sie-ro ven-ga un fo-glio mes-sag-gie-ro, e la vi-ta fug-gi-
wilt thou send a-to-ken, That thy faith re-mains un-broken, While I sigh for thy re-
Str. pizz. p
Edgar.
ti-va di spe-ran-ze nu-dri-rò. Io di te memo-ria vi-va sempre, o
turning? On that hope my heart shall live. While the flame of life is burn-ing, On thy
Moderato assai.
sempre legato
Lucy.
Ah! Ver-ran-no a te sul-l'a-u-re i
Ah! When twi-light shad-ows low-er, My
ca-ra, ser-be-rò.
mem-'ry I shall live.
Moderato assai.
pp Str pizz.
miei so-spi-ri ar-den-ti, u-drai nel mar che mor-mo-ra,
ar-dent pray'rs as-cend-ing, Will ask that joy on thee may show'r,
Ob. and Hn.
fp
l'e-co de' mie-i la-men-ti. Pen-san-do ch'io di ge-mi-ti mi
Our days of sor-row end-ing. On sighs and pray'rs I now shall live, Un-
Fl.

rinf. f
pa - sco e di do - lor, spar-gi un' a - ma - ra la - gri - ma su
til our part - ing's o'er; Ah, let this to - ken say to thee, I
accel.
que - sto pe - gno al - lor, ah! su que - sto pe - gno al - lor, ah! su
love thee ev - er - more, ah! I love thee ev - er more, ah! I
Fag.
accel.
Tutti.
string.
que - sto pe - gno al - lor, ah! su quel
love thee ev - er - more, I love thee
Tempo I.
pe - gno al - lor.
ev - er - more!
Ver - ran - no a te sul - l'a - u - re i miei so - spi - ri ar - den -
When twi - light shad - ows low - er, My ar - dent pray'rs as - cend -
Tempo I.
pp
fp
ti, u - drai nel mar che mor - mo - ra l'e - co de' miei la - men -
ing, Will ask that joy on thee may show'r, Our days of sor - row end -

rinf.
ti. Pen - san - do ch'io di ge - mi - ti mi pa - sco e di do - lor,
ing. On sighs and pray'rs I now shall live, Un - til our part - ing's o'er,
accel.
spar - gi un' a - ma - ra la - gri - ma su que - sto pe - gno al - lor, ah!
Ah, let this to - ken say to thee, I love thee ev - er - more, ah!
f accel.
Lucy.
string.
Ah! sì, su quel pe - gno al
Ah! I love thee ev - er -
su que - sto pe - gno al - lor, ah! su que - sto pe - gno al
I love thee ev - er - more, ah! I love thee ev - er -
string.
lor, Ed - gar - do
more, my Ed - gar
lor, ah! su quel pe - gno al - lor.
more, I love thee ev - er - more.
Poco più mosso.

Il tuo scrit - to sem - pre vi - va la me - mo - ria in me ter -
While the flame of life is burn - ing, On thy mem - 'ry I shall
Ca - ra!
Dear - est!
rà!
live!
Ah! Ver -
Ah! When
Sì, sì, Lu - ci - a, sì, sì.
Ah, dear-est Lu - cy, fare - well!
Ah! Ver -
Ah! When
rall.
Fl.
Ob.
rall. pp legato
Cl.
Fag.
Tempo I.
ran - no a me sul - l'a - u - re i tuoi so - spi - ri ar -
twi - light shad - ows low - er, My ar - dent pray'rs as -
Vln. Ob. Cl. with voice.
Harp.
Cor. and Fag. sustain.
Tymp.
den - ti, u - drò nel mar che mor - mo - ra
cend - ing, Will ask that joy on thee may show - er,
Tymp.

l'e - co de' mie - i la - men - ti. Pen - san - do che di
Our days of sor - row end - ing. On sighs and pray'rs I
l'e - co de' mie - i la - men - ti.
Our days of sor - row end - ing.
ge - mi - ti mi pa - sco e di do - lor,
now shall live un - til our part - ing's o'er.
Edgar.
spar - gi su que - sto pe - gno al -
Ah yes, I love thee ev - er -
Spar-gi un' a - ma - ra la - gri - ma su que - sto pe - gno al -
Ah! let this to - ken say to thee, I love thee ev - er -
p
string.
cresc.
lor, ah! su que - sto pe - gno al - lor, ah! su
more, ah! I love thee ev - er - more, ah! I
lor, ah! su que - sto pe - gno al - lor, ah! su
more, ah! I love thee ev - er - more, ah! I
f string.
fp

que - sto pe - gno al - lor, ah!
love thee ev - er - more, ah!
que - sto pe - gno al - lor, ah!
love thee ev - er - more, ah!
Più Allegro.
que - sto pe - gno al - lor,
yes, I love, yes, I love
que - sto pe - gno al - lor,
yes, I love, yes, I love
Più Allegro.
sì, sì, al - lor, sì,
thee ev - er - more, yes,
sì, sì, al - lor, sì,
thee ev - er - more, yes,
sì, al - lor!
ev - er - more!
sì, al - lor! Io par -
ev - er - more! Fare - well

Lucy.
- to. Ad - di - - o.
— then. Ah, fare - - well.
Edgar. rall. non tanto
a tempo
Ram - men - ta - ti, ne strin - ge il Ciel!
Re - mem - ber me, thoust plight - ed thy faith!
colla parte
(Lucy retires into the castle.)
Ed - gar - do!
I am thine.
(Exit Edgar.)
Ad - di - o!
Ah, fare - well!
f
f
f

End of Act I.

Act II.

Il Contratto nuziale. (The Marriage-contract.)

Nº 5. "Lucia fra poco a te verrà."

Introduction and Recit.

Apartments of Sir Henry Ashton.

A fe-steg-giar le noz-ze il-
With pomp to cel-e-brate the

lu-stri, già nel ca-stel-lo i no-bi-li pa-ren-ti giunser di mia fa-mi-glia; in
nuptial, I've bidden hither our friends and noble kinsmen; du-ly let them be welcom'd. Sir

(rising in extreme agitation.)

Norman.

breve Artu-ro qui vol-ge. E s'el-la per-ti-na-ce o-sas-se d'oppor-si? Non te-
Arthur, too, will come shortly. But what if she be stubborn, and dare to re-sist me? Fear it

mer: la lun-ga as-sen-za del tuo ne-mi-co, i fo-gli da noi ra-
not. Con-tin-ued ab-sence will have es-trang'd her, the let-ters we in-ter-

fp

pi-ti, e la bu-giar-da nuo-va ch'e-gli s'ac-ce-se d'al-tra
cept-ed, and the re-port sent fly-ing that he an-oth-er bride hath

fiam-ma, in co-re di Lu-ci-a spe-gne-ran-no il cie-co a-
chos-en, will rouse her to re-sent-ment, And to cast off her fool-ish

f

Henry.
mo-re. El-la s'a-van-za. Il si-mu-la-to fo-glio por-gi-mi.
pas-sion. See, where she com-eth. Where's the pretend-ed let-ter? give it me!
f
p
(Norman gives him a letter.)
Ed e-sci sul-la via che tragge al-la cit-tà re-gi-na di Scozia, e qui fra
And now to horse, upon the highway that doth lead to our King's royal cit-y, Proceed un-
f
Allegro.
(Exit Norman.)
plau-si e lie-te gri-da con-duci Ar-tu-ro.
til thou meetest Arthur, and bid him hither.
f
Nº 6. "Il pallor funesto, orrendo."
Recitative and Duet.
Larghetto. Lucy Ashton enters and stands near the doorway.
Recit. Henry.
Henry.
Piano.
Ob.
p
Ap-
Draw
(Lucy Ashton comes forward listlessly, looking fixedly at her brother.)
pres-sa-ti, Lu-ci-a.
near to me, oh, sis-ter!
a tempo

Spe - rai più lie - ta in que-sto dì ve-
With looks more joy-ful this day I thought to

der - ti, in que-sto dì, che d'I - me-neo le fa - ci s'ac-cen-do - no per
find thee, up-on the morn when love and all its bliss-es in-vite thy heart to

Larghetto.

te. Mi guar - di, e ta - ci?
joy. My sis - ter, why si - lent?

Cl.

Moderato.

Lucy.

Il pal-
If my

ff

tr

lor fu-ne - sto, or-ren - do, che ri - co-prè il vol - to mi - o,
cheek is blanch'd with ter - ror, Well thou knowest my cause of griev - ing;

p

ff

ti rim-pro - ve-ro ta-
Ah, re-nounce thy fa-tal
Vln.
pp
cen - do il mio stra - zio,
er - ror, See my weep - ing,
il mio do-lo - re. Per - do-
let me im-plore thee. Mine are
na - re ti pos - sa Id-di - o l'i - nu-
sor - rows past all re - liev - ing, Heav'n for-
cresc.
ma - no tuo ri-gor, per-do-nar-ti pos - sa Id-
give thy harsh re-solve; Mine are sor-rows past all re-
ff

di-o, ah! l'i-nu-ma-no tuo ri-gor,
lieving, Ah, heav'n for-give thy harsh re-solve,
l'i-nu-ma-no tuo ri-
heav'n for-give thy harsh re-
ff
gor, il tuo ri-gor, il tuo ri-gor, e il
solve, oh heav'n for-give thy harsh re-solve, for-
Henry.
mi-o do-lor!
give thee thy resolve!
A ra-
Ev-er-
tr

Meno mosso.
gion mi fe' spie - ta - to quel che t'ar - se in - de - gno af - fet - to;
more thou hast o - bey'd me; Wilt thou now in all re - sist — me?
pp
ff
ff
ma si tac - cia del pas -
Let a broth - er's love per -
Vln.
pp
sa - to; tuo fra - tel - lo, tuo fra -
suade — thee This un - hal - low'd, this un -
tel - lo so - no an - cor. Spen - ta è
hallow'd vow to dis - solve. Fond - ness and
li - ra nel - mi - o pet - to, spe - gni
du - ty, all — should as - sist me, That — thou

tu — l'in-sa - no a-mor, spen-ta è l'i-ra nel mio
yield to my — re-solve, Love and du-ty should as -
pet-to, spe - gni tu — l'in-sa-no a-mor, sì, — spe - gni
sist me, That — thou yield to — my — re - solve, yes, that thou
cresc.
tu l'in - sa-no a-mor, ah, spe-gni
yield thee to my — re-solve, ah, that thou
ff
tu l'in - sa - no a - mor, l'in - sa - no a -
yield to — my re - solve, to — my — re -
mor, l'in - sa - no a - mor, spe - gni tu l'in-sa - no a - mor. No - bil
solve, to — my — re - solve, that thou yield to my — re - solve. Come, thy

Più Allegro.
Lucy.
Henry.
Lucy.
spo-so — Ces-sa, ces-sa! Co-me? Ad al-tr'uom — giu-
husband — Ah, be si-lent! Where-fore? To an-oth-er I've
ff
Henry.
(angrily.)
Lucy.
Henry.
ra-i mi-a fè. Nol po-te-vi — En-ri-co! Nol po-
plight-ed my faith. 'Tis not law-ful. Oh, broth-er! 'Tis not
Lucy.
Henry.
(restraining himself.)
te-vi — Ad al-tro giu-ra-i, ad al-tro giu-rai mia fe. Ba-sti!
law-ful. My heart is an-oth-er's, to him I have giv'n my faith. Si-lence!
(giving her the letter he received from Norman.)
rall.
Que-sto foglio appien ti di-ce qual cru-del, qual em-pio a-ma-sti.
Read this let-ter, it will tell thee, to a trai-tor thou hast giv'n it.
colla parte
Allegro.
(Lucy reads the letter; struck with horror and dismay, she is seized with a sudden trem-bling.)
Leg-gi.
Read it!
p
cresc.

Lucy.

Ah! il co-re mi bal-zò!

Ah! oh, heav'n, my heart will break!

Henry. (running to her assistance)

Tu va-cil-li!—

Thou art trembling—

Lucy.

Me in-fe-li-ce! ahi! la fol-go-re piom-bò!

Ah, what sor-row! Ah!— The bolt of fate hath fall'n!

p meno mosso

Larghetto.

Corno

pp

Cl.

Tromba

Bssn.

Strings.

Lucy.

Sof-fri-va nel pian-to, lan-gui-a nel do-lo-re, la

In si-lence and sor-row I lan-guish'd un-re-pin-ing, One

Cor.& Fag.

spe - - me, la vi - ta ri po - - si in un
hope shone be-fore me, that I was be-
affrett. e cresc. di forza
cor, l'i-stan - te di mor - te è giun - to per
lov'd, In mer - cy re-call then the words thou hast
affrett. e cresc. di forza
rall.
p
me! quel co - - re in-fe-
said, For if he is
colla parte
Henry.
de - le ad al - tra ad al-tra si diè! Un fol-le t'ac-
faith - less, I would but that I were dead. I can-not re-
Strings Cor. & Fag.
pp
Cor.
ce - se, un per - fi-do a - mo - re; tra - di - sti il tuo
call them, the trai-tor de - sign - ing Thy heart hath en-
Corni III & IV.

Lucy.
Oh Di - o!
Oh heav - en!
san - gue per vil se - dut - to - re, ma de - gna del cie - lo ne a - ve - sti mer-
snared, but he nev - er hath lov'd thee, Arouse thee, and scorn him, bring pride to thy
l.h.
Ahi - mè! L'i - stan - te tre -
Ah me! In mer - cy re -
cè: quel co - re in - fe - de - le ad al - tra si diè. Un fol - le t'ac -
aid; His im - age will soon from thy mem - o - ry fade. A - rouse thee, and
Cl.
men - do è giun - to per me, sì, quel co - re in - fe - de - le ad al - tra si
call then the word thou hast said, for if he is faith - less, for if he is
ce - se, un per - fi - do a mo - re; tra - di - sti il tuo san - gue per vil se - dut -
scorn him, he nev - er hath lov'd thee, A - rouse thee and scorn him, he never hath
Fl.
Ob.
die - de, quel co - re in - fe - de - le ad al - tra si diè, quel co -
faith - less, I would I were dead, Yes, I would I were dead. A - las!
to - re, ma de - gna dal cie - lo ne a - ve - sti mer - cè: quel co -
lov'd thee, His im - age will soon from thy mem - o - ry fade, Ah, yes!
f
f

re in-fe - de - le, quel co - re in - fe - de - le ad al - tra si
if he is faith - less, Ah yes, if he is faith-less, I would I were
re in-fe - de - le, quel co - re in - fe - de - le ad al - tra si
his im-age soon will, Yes, soon will from thy mem'-ry, thy mem-o-ry
diè, ad al - tra si diè, ad al - tra, ad
dead, I would I were dead, for if he is
diè, ad al - tra si diè, sì, sì, si diè, ad al - tra, ad
fade, a-rouse thee, and scorn, ah, yes, scorn him, a-rouse thee, and
al - tra, ad al - tra si diè!
faith less, I would I were dead!
al - tra, ad al - tra si diè!
scorn him, bring pride to thy aid!
(Festive music is heard in the distance.)
Lucy.
Henry.
Che fi - a! Suo-
What mu-sic? A
Vivace

nar di giu - bi - lo sen - ti la ri - va.
strain of fes - tive mirth, All are re - joic - ing.
ff
Henry.
Lucy.
Eb - be - ne? Giun - ge il tuo spo - so.
And wherefore? To wel - come thy hus-band.
p
Lucy.
Henry.
Un bri - vi - do mi cor - se per le ve - ne! A te s'ap - pre - sta il
A dead - ly chill be - numbs my scatter'd sens - es! The nuptial hour ap -
Lucy.
La tom - ba, la tom - ba a me s'ap - pre - sta!
Ah! no, 'tis the hour of my doom ap - proach - es!
ta - la - mo. O - ra fa -
proach - es. Spare me thy
f
p

Meno Allegro.
Ho su-gl'oc-chi un vel!
Ah! my sight grows dim!
p
ta-le è que - - sta! M'o-di! Spen-to è Gu-gliel-mo... a-
vain re-proach - es! Lis-ten to what I tell thee: Since
Meno Allegro.
Fag. I.
Viole
Fag. II.
scen - de-re vedre - mo il tro-no Ma-ri-a Pro-
Wil - liam lives no more, our par-ty is fal-len, Up-
Vlns.
stra - ta è nel - la pol - ve-re la par - te ch'io se-
on the throne of Scot - land now will reign the hat - ed
Viola.
Ah! io tre-mo!
Woe up - on us!
gui-a
Dal pre-ci-pi - zio Ar-tu-ro può sot-
Ma-ry
In this sad hour none can from ru-in
Vlns.

Ed i - o? ed
And I am the

trar - mi, sol e - gli-
save me but Ar - thur_

Tutti

ff

i - o? En-
vic - tim? Oh,

Sal - var mi de - vi.
Yes, thou must save me.

ri - co! Ad al - tri giu - ra - i.
broth - er! My faith I have plight - ed.

Vie-ni al-lo spo - so. De - vi sal-
Come to the nup - tials. That was in

a piacere

Ma_ Oh ciel! oh ciel!
Ah! (about to go) Ah me, ah me!

var - mi. Il de - vi.
mad-ness. Twas mad - ness.

ff

pp

Henry. (returning, with rapid, tho' energetic accent.)
Vivace.
Se tra-dir-mi tu po-tra-i, la mia sor-te è
To my ru-in then con-sent-ing, Cold and si-lent, thou
p
Strings pizz. Cor. & Fag.
già com-pi-ta; tu m'in-vo-lio-no-re e vi-ta, tu la
yet dost brave me, From the scaf-fold naught can save me, Be my
Fl. & Cl.
Poco meno.
scu-re ap-pre-sti a me. Ne' tuoi so-gni mi ve-dra-i,
blood up-on thy head. Cease thy use-less, vain la-ment-ing,
Tempo I.
om-bra i-ra-ta e mi-nac-cio-sa! quel-la scu-re san-gui-
Go, and to the foe be-tray me, Let thy sense-less pas-sion
Cl.
Cor.
no-sa sta-rà sem-pre in-nan zi a te, sta-rà sem-pre, sta-rà
sway thee, But my vengeance ye both shall dread; yes, my vengeance, yes, my
Fl. Ob.
Cl. Vln.

sem - pre in-nan - zi a te, sta-rà sem-pre, sem-pre, sem - pre in-
ven-geance ye both shall dread, yes, my vengeance, yes, my ven - geance ye
Tutti
f
nan-zi a te! Tu che ve - di il pian - to mi - o, tu che
both shall dread! Oh, have mer - cy, pit - ying heav-en, Read the
Lucy. (turning her tearful eyes to heaven)
p
leg-gi in que - sto co - re, se re-spin - to il mio do - lo - re,
heart that bows be - fore thee, Guide my spir - it, I im-plore thee,
co-me in ter-ra, in ciel non è; tu mi to - glie - ter - no Id -
By thee on-ly I would be led. See my heart with sor-row
di - o, que - sta vi - ta di - spe - ra - ta, io son tan - to
riv - en, See my life for - ev - er blighted, Ah, un-less to

ff
sven - tu - ra - ta, che la mor - te è un ben per me, sì, la
him u - nit - ed, Take me from the doom I dread, take me,
f
mor - te, sì, la mor - te è un ben per me, sì, la mor - te, sì, la
take me from the doom, from the doom I dread, take me, take me from the
mor - te è un ben per me.
doom, from the doom I dread.
Henry.
A te s'ap -
Thy nup - tial
Vln.
pre - sta il ta - la - mo.
hour is drawing nigh.
Lucy.
Ah! la tom - ba!
Ah! be si - lent!
Henry.
Sal - var mi de - vi.
'Tis thou must save me.
Lucy.
Ho su - gl'oc - chi un vel!
Ah! my sight grows dim!
Ah! Se tra - dir - mi tu po -
Ah! To my ru - in then con -

tra - i, la mia sor - te è già com - pi - ta, tu m'in -
sent - ing, Cold and si - lent thou yet dost brave me, From the
vo - li o - no - re e vi - ta, tu la scu - re ap - pre - sti a
scaf - fold naught can save me, Be my blood up - on thy
me.
head.
Lucy.
Meno.
Ah, mi to - gli, e - ter - no Id - di - o,
See my heart with sor - row riv - en,
Meno.
que - sta vi - ta di - spe - ra - ta, io son tan - to sven - tu -
See my life for - ev - er blight - ed, Ah, un - less with him u -
a tempo
Mi ve - drai, om - bra i - ra - ta, quel - la scu - re san - gui -
To the foe then be - tray me, let thy fa - tal pas - sion
a tempo
ra - ta, che la mor - te è un ben per me, sì, la mor - te, sì, la
nit - ed, Take me from the fate I dread, take me, take me from the
no - sa sta - rà sem - pre in - nan - zi a te, sem - pre, sem - pre, sem - pre,
sway thee, But my ven - geance ye shall dread, yes, my ven - geance, yes my

mor - te è un ben per me, sì, la mor - te, sì, la mor - -
fate, from the fate I dread, take me, take me from the fate
sem - pre in - nan - zi a te, sem - pre, sem - pre, sem - pre, sem - -
ven - geance ye both shall dread, Yes, my vengeance, yes, my ven - -
- te è un ben per me, la mor - te è un ben è un
ah, from the fate I dread, ah, take me from the fate
- pre in - nan - zi a te, sì, sem - pre, sem - pre in -
- geance ye both shall dread, ah yes, my ven - geance
ben per me, sì, sì, la mor - - - - -
that I dread, ah, take me, take
nan - zi a te, in - nan - zi a te, a
ye shall dread, my ven - geance ye shall
ff
te, sì, la mor - te è un ben, è un ben
me from the fate, from the fate that I dread,
te, sì, sì, sta - rà sem - pre in - nan - -
dread, yes, my ven - geance ye both, ah, yes,

per me, è un ben per
the fate, the fate I
zi a te, in - - nan - zi a
both shall dread, Yes, ye both shall
me, è un ben per me,
dread, the fate I dread,
te, in - - nan - zi a te,
dread, my ven - geance ye both
è un ben, è un ben, è un
the fate, the fate, the
a te, a te, a
shall dread, ah, yes, ye
(She sinks on a chair)
ben per me.
fate I dread.
(Exit hastily.)
te, a te.
both shall dread.

Nº 7. "Ah, cedi, cedi.,,

Recitative and Aria.

Cantabile.
p Strings
Piano.
calando
p
f
Lucy Ashton. (Seeing Bide-the-Bent approaching, anxiously hastens to meet him.)
Eb - ben?
What news?
Bide - the - Bent.
Di tua spe - ran - za l'ul - ti - mo rag - gio tra - mon -
Ah do not ask me! Naught but of woe have I to
tò! Cre - de - i, al tuo so - spet - to, che il fra - tel chiu - des - se tut - te le
tell. Suspecting that to mis - lead thee, ti - dings from thy lov - er were in - ter -
strade on - de sul franco suo - lo, all' uom che amar giu - ra - sti, non giunges - ser tue
rupted, or that thy brother's harshness withheld from him thy letters, so as quite to di -

nuo-ve: io stes-so un foglio da te ver-ga-to per se-cu-ra ma-no re-car gli
vide you; one of thy letters came to my hands by a trusty bearer. I know it

fe-ci— in-va-no! Ta-ce mai sem-pre. Quel si-
reach'd him— 'Twas use-less! Still he is si-lent. Doubt no

len-zio as-sai d'in-fe-del-tà ti par-la! **Lucy.** E me con-si-gli? **Bide-the-Bent.** Di pie-gar-ti al de-
longer, his silence tells that he is faithless. What dost thou counsel? That thou yield to thy

sti-no. **Lucy.** E il giu-ra-men-to? **Bide-the-Bent.** Tu pur va-neg-gi! I nu-zi-a-li vo-ti che il mi-
brother. The vows I plighted? They were un-lawful! Vows that are rashly spoken, without

ni-stro di Di-o non be-ne-di-ce, nè il ciel, nè il mon-do ri-co-no-sce. **Lucy.** Ah!
sanction from God or priest, are not binding; from them this moment I re-lease thee. Ah!

ce - de per - su - a - sa la men - te, ma sor - do al - la ra -
leave me, thou per - suad - est my rea - son, but nev - er can this

Bide-the-Bent. **Lucy.**

gion re - si - ste il co - re! Vin - cer - lo e for - za. Oh sven - tu - ra - to a - mo - re!
heart yield love to reason. Make but an ef - fort. Ah me, un - hap - py! I cannot!

f

Bide-the-Bent. Cantabile.

Ah! ce - di, ce - di, o più scia - gu - re ti so -
Ah! 'tis to suc - cor thy hap - less broth - er That I

Tutti

Strings pizz.

f p Cl.

vra - stan, ti so - vra - sta - no, in - fe - li - ce. Per le te - ne - re mie
ask thee, that I ask thee to o - bey me, By the mem - 'ry of thy

Fag. & Cor.

cu - re, per l'e - stin - ta ge - ni - tri - ce, il pe -
moth - er Let a sis - ter's du - ty sway thee; Cast a -

f p

cresc.
ri - glio, il pe-ri - glio d'un fra-tel - lo, il pe-ri-glio d'un fra -
way, oh cast a-way a fleet-ing pas - sion, cast a-way, a fleet-ing
cresc.
f
tel-lo deh ti muo-va, e can-gi il cor. O la
pas-sion, And to us thy heart re - store. If thy
Tutti
f p
ma-dre, o la ma-dre nel-l'a-vel-lo fre-me-rà, fre-me-rà per te d'or-
life by wayward fan-cy thou wilt fash-ion I dis-own, I disown thee ev-er-
ror. Ah, ce-di, ce-di, il pe-ri-glio d'un fra-tel-lo ti com-
more, Ah, cast a-way then, cast a-way a fleet-ing pas-sion, And to
fp
f
Allegro.
Lucy.
mo-va e can-gi, e can-gi il cor. Ta - ci, ta - ci!
us, yes, to us thy heart, thy heart re-store. Thou art cru - el!
Ob.
Cl.
ff

Bide-the-Bent.
Lucy.
Bide-the -Bent.
No, no, ce - di. Ah! ah! ta - ci. La
'Tis to save thee. Ah no, leave me! Thy
cresc.
Fag.
Ah! ah! ta - ci. Ah! vin -
Ah, how cru - el! Ah! I
ma - dre il fra - tel - lo.
broth - er will be ru - ined!
ce - sti. Non son tan - to sna - tu -
yield then! Not by me shall he be
Ob.
Fl.
Bide-the-Bent.
ra - ta. Oh! qual gio - ja in me tu de - sti!
ru - ined. Ah! what say'st thou? Thou wilt o - bey me?
cresc.
rinf.
oh qual nu - be hai dis - si - pa - ta!
Ah what joy thy words a - wa - ken!

Ah!
Ah!
Qual gio - - ja!
thou'lt save him!
Bass pizz
Moderato.
Wood
Al ben de' tuoi qual vit - ti - ma of - fri, Lucia, te
If it be done in sac - ri - fice, For a be - lov - ed
Strings and Hn.
stes - sa; e tan - to sacri - fi - zio scritto nel ciel sa - rà,
broth - er, On high 'twill be re - cord - ed, Heav'n will thy fu - ture guard,
nel ciel sa - rà. Of - fri, Lu - cia, te stes - sa,
yes, heav'n will guard. For a be - lov - ed broth - er,

e tan-to sa-cri - fi - zio scrit-to nel ciel sa - rà. Se la pietà de -
On high'twill be re - cord - ed, Heav'n will thy fu-ture guard; She who renounces
Hn. and Tromb.
gli uo-mi-ni a te non fia con-ces - sa, v'è un Di-o, v'è un Dio che ter - ge-re il
earth-ly joy That she may bless an-oth - er, The angels thro' life her steps will lead, In
cresc.
cresc.
pian - to tuo sa - prà. Se la pie-tà de - gli uo - mi-ni
death the prize a - ward; She who renounces earth - ly joy
p
ff
tr
a te non fia con-ces - sa, v'è un Di-o, v'è un Di-o, che ter-ge-re il pian-to tuo sa -
That she may bless an-oth - er, The angels thro' life her steps will lead, In death the prize a -
prà, il pian - to tuo sa - prà, il pian - to tuo sa -
ward in death the prize a - ward, in death the prize a -
ff

Lucy.

Più allegro.

cresc.

Gui - da-mi tu,_ tu_ reg-gi -mi, son fuo-ri_ di_ me stes - sa!
Lead me,and coun-sel_ me a - right, And let me save my broth - er!

prà. Sì, fi - glia, co -
ward. Thou'lt save him, take

Vl.& Cl.

Più allegro.

p

cresc.

Tutti.

Lun-go,crudel sup-pli - zio la vi - ta a me_ sa - rà!
Dreary will be my fu - ture, If now I my faith dis - card!

rag - gio! Qual nube hai disgom-bra-ta! Oh fi - glia mia, co -
cour - age, What joy thy words a - waken! Oh daughter mine, take

ff

Tempo I.

Sì, gui - da-mi, sì, sì.
Yes, counsel me a - - right.

rag - gio! Ah! Al ben de'tuoi qual
cour - age! ah! If it be done in

Tempo I.

p

vit - ti-ma of - fri, Lucia, te stes - sa, e tan - to sa-cri -
sac - rifice For a belov - ed broth - er, On high 'twill be re -

fi - zio scrit - to nel ciel sa - rà, nel ciel sa -
cord - ed, Heav'n will thy fu - ture guard, yes, heav'n will
ff
p
Lucy.
Nel ciel sa - rà, sì.
Yes, heav'n will guard me!
rà. Of - fri, Lucia, te stes - sa,
guard. For a be - lov - ed broth - er,
ff
p
e tan - to sa - cri - fi - zio scrit - to nel ciel sa - rà.
On high 'twill be re - cord - ed, Heav'n will thy fu - ture guard.
Ah!
Ah!
Oh Di - o! Son fuor di me!
Ah, wretched will be my lot!
Se la pietà de - gli uo - mi - ni a te non fia con - ces - sa,
She who renounces earth - ly joy, That she may bless an - oth - er,

In - gra - to!
Oh, Ed - gar,
Di - o, v'è un Dio, che ter - ge - re il pian - to tuo sa -
an - gels thro' life her steps will lead, In death the prize a -
(weeping.)
Ed - gar - do in - gra - to!
thou hast for - got me!
prà. Se la pie - tà de - gli uo - mi - ni a te non fia con -
ward. She who renounces earth - ly joy, That she may bless an -
ces - sa, v'è un Di - o, v'è un Di - o, che ter - ge - re il pian - to tuo sa -
oth - er, The an - gels thro' life her steps will lead, In death the prize a -
prà, il pian - to tuo sa - prà, il pian - to tuo sa -
ward, in death the prize a - ward, in death the prize a -
Più allegro.
prà, il pian - to tuo sa - prà, il pian - to tuo sa -
ward, in death the prize a - ward, in death the prize a -

Gui - da - mi, vin - ce - sti, Ah!
Coun - sel me and guide me, Ah!
prà, ah, sì, sa - prà, il pian - to tuo
ward, the an - - gels will in death the prize
ah! ah!
ah me!
sa - - prà.
a - - ward.
Nº 8. "Per poco fra le tenebre."
Finale II. _ Chorus and Cavatina.
(A festive hall, prepared for the reception of Sir Arthur Bucklaw. At the back a practicable doo
Moderato mosso.
Piano.
Vl.
Ob.& Cl.
Fl.

1
p
Strings, Cor. & Fag.
SOPRANO.
Per te d'im-men-so giu-bi-lo tut-to s'av-vi-va in-
Hail to the hap-py brid-al day, Hence, ev'-ry thought of
TENOR.
Per te d'im-men-so giu-bi-lo tut-to s'av-vi-va in-
Hail to the hap-py brid-al day, Hence, ev'-ry thought of
BASS.
Per te d'im-men-so giu-bi-lo tut-to s'av-vi-va in-
Hail to the hap-py brid-al day, Hence, ev'-ry thought of
fp
tor-no, per te veg-giam ri-na-sce-re
sor-row, Let ev'-ry heart with hope be gay,
tor-no, per te veg-giam ri-na-sce-re
sor-row, Let ev'-ry heart with hope be gay,
tor-no, per te veg-giam ri-na-sce-re
sor-row, Let ev'-ry heart with hope be gay,

del - la spe-ran - za il gior - no, qui l'a - mi - stà ti
Bright be to thee each mor - row, Friend - ship and love will
gui - da, qui ti con - du - ce a - mo - re,
guide thee Far from temp - ta - tion and dan - ger,
tut - to rav - vi - va in - tor - no, qui ti con - du - ce a -
May ev' - ry good be - tide thee, That on thy head we im

mor, qual a - stro in not - te in - fi - da,
plore, May naught e'er on earth di - vide ye,
mor, qual a - stro in not - te in - fi - da,
plore, May naught e'er on earth di - vide ye,
mor, qual a - stro in not - te in - fi - da,
plore, May naught e'er on earth di - vide ye,
qual ri - so nel do - lor; qual a - stro in not - te in -
Who now will part no more; Be thou to grief a
qual ri - so nel do - lor; qual a - stro in not - te in -
Who now will part no more; Be thou to grief a
qual ri - so nel do - lor; qual a - stro in not - te in -
Who now will part no more; Be thou to grief a
fi - da, qual ri - so nel do - lor.
stran - ger, From this thy brid - al hour.
fi - da, qual ri - so nel do - lor.
stran - ger, From this thy brid - al hour.
fi - da, qual ri - so nel do - lor.
stran - ger, From this thy brid - al hour.

Sir Arthur Bucklaw.
Meno mosso.
Per po - - co fra le te - ne-bre spa
By For - - tune's fic-kle frowns be-tray'd, Th
Ob. & Strings
Vl. & Bassi pizz.
Hrn.
rì la vo - stra stel - la: io la fa - rò ri -
star hath long been shroud - ed, Now it shall break from
Cl. with voice.
Fl.
sor - ge - re più ful - gi - da, più bel - la. La
sor - row's shade, And beam with light un-cloud - ed. A
man mi por-gi, En-ri - co, ti strin - - gi a que-st
broth - er's hand I of - fer, A broth - - er's faith I
cor, a te ne ven - go a - mi - - co, fr
swore, My hand and for - tune I prof - - fer To

tel - lo e di - fen - sor.
her — whom I a - dore.
Tempo I.
Chorus.
Ah!
Ah!
Per te d'im-men - so
Hail to the hap - py
Vlns. & Fag.
Tutti as before
fp Tempo I.
giu - bi - lo tut - to s'av-vi - va in - tor - no,
brid - al — day, Hence ev'- ry thought of sor - row,
per te veg-giam ri - na - sce - re del - la spe-ran - za il
Le ev' - ry heart with hope be — gay, Bright be to thee each

gior - no, qui l'a - mi - stà ti gui - da,
mor - row, Friend - ship and love will guide thee,
gior - no, qui l'a - mi - stà ti gui - da,
mor - row, Friend - ship and love will guide thee,
gior - no, qui l'a - mi - stà ti gui - da,
mor - row, Friend - ship and love will guide thee,
qui ti con - du - ce a - mo - re, tut - to rav - vi - va in
Far from temp - ta - tion and dan - ger, May ev - 'ry good be -
qui ti con - du - ce a - mo - re, tut - to rav - vi - va in
Far from temp - ta - tion and dan - ger, May ev - 'ry good be -
qui ti con - du - ce a - mo - re, tut - to rav - vi - va in
Far from temp - ta - tion and dan - ger, May ev - 'ry good be -
tor - no, qui ti con - du - ce a - mor, qual
tide thee, That on thy head we im - plore, May
tor - no, qui ti con - du - ce a - mor, qual
tide thee, That on thy head we im - plore, May
tor - no, qui ti con - du - ce a - mor, qual
tide thee, That on thy head we im - plore, May

Arthur.
A te ne ven-go a - mi - co, fra-tel - lo e di-fen -
For - tune and hand I prof - fer To her whom I a -
a - stro in not-te in - fi - da, qual ri - so nel do -
naught e'er on earth di - vide ye, Who now will part no
a - stro in not-te in - fi - da, qual ri - so nel do -
naught e'er on earth di - vide ye, Who now will part no
f
so - re, a te ne ven-go a - mi - co, fra -
dore, For - tune and hand I prof - fer To
lor, qual a-stro in not - te in - fi - da, qual
more, Be thou to grief a stran - ger, From
lor, qual a-stro in not - te in - fi - da, qual
more, Be thou to grief a stran - ger, From
8

Più allegro.
tel - lo e di - fen - sor, fra - tel - lo e di - - fen -
her whom I a - dore. Ah no, let naught di -
ri - so nel do - lor.
this thy bri - dal hour.
ri - so nel do - lor. e di - fen
this thy bri - dal hour. May naught di
Più allegro.
sor, fra - tel - lo e di - - - - fen - - - -
vide us, who will part no
e di - - - fen - - - -
They part no
sor, fra - tel - lo e di - - - fen - - - -
vide ye, who will part no
ff
sor, di - fen - sor, di - fen - sor, fra - tel - lo e
more, part no more, part no more, ah no, we
sor, di - fen - sor, di - fen - sor, e
more, part no more, part no more, ye
sor, di - fen - sor, di - fen - sor, fra - tel - lo e
more, part no more, part no more, Ah, no, ye
sf

di - - - fen - - - sor, a te ne
part no more, we part no
di - - - fen - - - sor, e di - fen -
part no more, ye part no
di - - - fen - - - sor, e di - fen -
part no more, ye part no
ven - go di - fen - sor.
more, we part no more.
sor, e di - fen - sor.
more, ye part no more.
sor, e di - fen - sor.
more, ye part no more.
p
f

Nº 9. "Chi mi frena in tal momento."

Finale II. _ Recitative and Quartet.

Henry.
sì, sì, m'è no-to. Soverchia e la me-sti - zia, ma pian-ge la
Yes, I ob-serv'd it. She's sad and heav-y-heart - ed, but 'tis for her
f
f
Arthur.
ma - - dre. Or sol-vi un dub-bio.
moth - - - er. One question an-swer:
ff
p
Fa - ma, fa-ma suo-nò ch'Ed-gar - do so-
Late - ly ru-mor hath said that Ed - gar hath
vr'es - sa, so-vr'es-sa te - me-ra - rio al-za - re o-sò lo
rash - ly, hath mad-ly dared to love her, and that his fa - tal
calando
Henry.
sguar - do te-me-ra - - rio. È
pas - sion by thy sis - ter The
cresc.
p

ve - ro, è ve - ro, quel fol-le ar-di - a, ma
mad - man, 'tis true, he hath dared to love her, but
Arthur.
Ah!
Well?
SOPRANO.
S'a-van-za qui Lu-ci - a, s'a-
Be-hold the bride, the peer-less one, be-
TENOR.
S'a-van-za qui Lu-ci - a, s'a-
Be-hold the bride, the peer-less one, be-
BASS.
S'a-van-za qui Lu-ci - a, s'a-
Be-hold the bride, the peer-less one, be-
Chorus.
Tutti
Henry.
(to Arthur.)
Andante.
(Enter Lucy supported by Bide-the-Bent and Alice. She is in great despondency.)
Pian-ge la ma-dre e-stin-ta.
Those tears are for her moth-er.
van - za.
hold her.
Andante.
Strings
'Cello
Fag.

(presenting Arthur to Lucy, who shrinks from him.)
(whispers to Lucy)
Ec-co il tuo spo-so.
There comes thy husband.
(In-cau-ta! per-der mi
(Be cautious! wilt thou un-
Lucy.
(Gran Di - o!)
Oh mer - cy!)
Arthur.
Ti piac-cia i vo - ti ac - co - glie-re del
Oh fair - est, deign to re-ceive the vows my
Henry.
vuo-i?)
do me?)
(Gran Di-o!)
Oh heaven!
te - ne-ro a-mor mi - o.
heart would fond - ly plight thee.
(going towards the table on which lies the marriage-contract, and interrupting Arthur.)
(In-cau-ta!) O - mai si com - pia il ri - to. T'ap-
(Be cautious!) 'Tis time to sign the con-tract; come,
Vln.
Ob.
Cl.

(Io va - do al
(My death-war - rant
(He goes to the table and signs the deed. Bide-the-Bent and Alice lead the trembling Lucy to the table.)
Oh dol - - ce in - vi - to!
Oh rap - - t'rous mo - ment!
pres - sa.
Ar - thur!
Bide-the-Bent.
(Reg - - gi, buon
(Heav - - en, do
Vln.
p
calando
Lucy.
sa - - cri - fi - - - - zio! me
he is sign - - - - ing! Ah,
Henry.
(Non e - si - tar! Scri - vi,
(O - bey at once, sign it,
Bide-the-Bent.
Dio, l'af - flit - - - ta.)
thou sus - tain her.)
Cl.
cresc.
Lucy.
(Lucy signs the contract.)
mi - se - ra!)
wretch - ed me!)
(La mia con - dan - na ho
(Now naught but death can re -
Henry.
scri - vi!)
sign it!)
calando

Allegro mosso.
Henry.
Lucy.
(leans upon Bide-the-Bent.)
Allegro.
scrit-ta!) (Re-spi-ro!) (Io ge - lo ed ar - do! io man-
lease me!) ('Tis o-ver!) (My heart burns and freez-es! Oh help
Tutti.
Viole & Cello.
Fag. sustain.
Lucy.
co!)
me!)
Alice.
(The door opens.)
Qual_ fra - gor! Chi giunge?
Who_ is this! a stranger?
Edgar. (His features concealed by a cloak, appears at the back.)
(With a terrible voice.)
Ed - gar-
'Tis Ed-
Arthur.
Qual_ fra - gor! Chi giunge?
Who_ is this! a stranger?
Henry.
Qual_ fra - gor! Chi giunge?
Who_ is this! a stranger?
Bide-the-Bent.
Qual_ fra - gor! Chi giunge?
Who_ is this! a stranger?
Qual_ fra - gor! Chi giunge?
Who_ is this! a stranger?
Qual_ fra - gor! Chi giunge?
Who_ is this! a stranger?
Qual_ fra - gor! Chi giunge?
Who_ is this! a stranger?
cresc.
ff
ff

(falls fainting.)
Ed - gar - do! Oh ful - mi - ne!
'Tis Ed - gar! Oh thun - der - bolt!
Ed - gar - do! Oh ter - ror!
'Tis Ed - gar! Day of woe!
do!
gar!
Ed - gar - do! Oh ter - ror!
'Tis Ed - gar! Day of woe!
Ed - gar - do! Oh ter - ror!
'Tis Ed - gar! Day of woe!
Ed - gar - do! Oh ter - ror!
'Tis Ed - gar! Day of woe!
Ah! Ed - gar - do! Oh ter - ror!
Ah! 'Tis Ed - gar! Day of woe!
Ah! Ed - gar - do! Oh ter - ror!
Ah! 'Tis Ed - gar! Day of woe!
Ah! Ed - gar - do! Oh ter - ror!
Ah! 'Tis Ed - gar! Day of woe!
f

(General consternation. Alice, aided by some ladies, raises Lucy and leads her to a seat.)
Alice.
Ed - gar-do!
Oh Ed-gar!
Bide-the-Bent.
Oh ter - ror!
Day of woe!
Ed - gar-do!
Lord Ed-gar!
Oh ter - ror!
Day of woe!
Oh ter - ror!
Day of woe!
f
p
Cl. & Corni.
p rall.
Larghetto. Edgar. (aside.) p
Chi mi fre - na in tal mo-me - to? chi tron-
What from ven - geance yet re-strains me, Words suf-
Henry. (aside.) p
Chi raf-fre - na il mio fu - ro - re, e la
What from ven - geance yet re-strains_me, Will he
Larghetto.
Strings pizz.
pp e sempre cresc.
Cl. sustain.

cò del-l'i-re il cor - so? Il suo duo - lo, il suo spa - ven - to son la
fice not to up - braid thee, E'en the ter - ror that thus en - chains thee, Proves that
man che al bran-do cor - se? Del - la mi-se-ra in fa - vo - re nel mio
mad - ly dare up - braid her? Ah, she dreads me, and dis - dains me, Nev - er
Bssn.
pro - va, son la pro-va d'un ri - mor - so! Ma, qual ro - sa i-na-ri -
false - ly, proves that false-ly thou'st be - tray'd me! As a rose 'mid tempest
f
p
pet - to un gri - do sor - se! È mio san - gue! l'ho tra -
more will I thus per - suade her! Day of wrath, what will be thy
Cl.
fp
di - ta, el - la sta fra mor-te e vi - ta! Io son vin - to, son com -
bend-ing, Grief and guilt thy heart are rend-ing, Thy des - pair - ing looks dis -
di - ta! El - la sta fra mor-te e vi - ta! Ah! che spe - gne-re non
end - ing! Fur-ther grief may be im - pend-ing! Her des-pair - ing looks a -
Fl.
Cl.
fp

(turning to Alice)
Lucy.
Io spe-
'Twas my
Edgar.
affrett.
mos. - so! t'a - mo,in - gra - ta, t'a - mo, t'a - mo,in-gra-ta, t'a - mo an-
arm me, Faith-less maid-en, faith-less maid, a - las, I love thee
Henry.
affrett.
pos - so i ri - mor - si del mio co - re, del mio
larm me, Name-less ter - rors, name-less fears my bo - som
Bide-the-Bent.
(Aside.)
Qual ter-
Oh, may
affrett.
rai che a me la vi- -ta tron-ca a - ves- - se il mio spa-
hope that death would hide me From a doom of shame and
cor!
still.
cor! È mio san - gue! l'ho tra- -
fill! Ah, she dreads me, and dis- -
ri- -bi - le mo - men - to! più for - mar non so pa-
heav'n in mer - cy guide thee In this hour of wrath and
Fl. & Cl. with voice.
pp

ven- -to, ma la mor- -te non m'a-i- -ta, vi-vo a
an- -guish, But that com- -fort is de-nied me, In de-
Chi mi fre-na in tal mo-men-to?
What restrains me From deeds of ven-geance?
di- -ta! io l'hotra-di-ta!
dains me! he'll not upbraid her!
ro- -le! den-sa nu- -be di spa-ven- -to par ch
an- -guish, Tho' af-flic- -tion new be-tide thee, Not fo
cor per mio tor-men-to! Da' miei lu- -mi cad-de il
spair I yet must lan-guish, None will coun- -sel, none wil
ma chi? chi? Co-m
oh, false-hood! Like a
ah! sì, sì! el-la sta
ah! ah no! never-more,
co- -prai rai del so- -le! Co-me ro- -sa i-na-ri-
ev- -er shalt thou lan-guish, Like a rose 'mid tempest
Cl.
fp

ve - lo, mi tra - dì la - ter - ra e il cie - lo! Vor - rei
aid me, Heav'n and earth have both be - tray'd me, Love, do
ro - sa i - na - ri - di - ta el - la sta fra mor - te e
rose to the tempest bending, Grief and guilt thy heart are
fra mor - te e vi - ta, fra mor - te e vi -
no more I'll per - suade her, no more per - suade
di - ta, el - la sta fra mor - te e vi - ta, chi per
bend - ing, Pale re - morse thy heart is rend - ing, Oh, may
8
Fl.
fp
pian - ge - re, e non pos - so, m'ab - ban - do - na, m'ab - ban -
thou with cour - age arm me, give me strength, oh give me
vi - ta! In - gra - ta, t'a - mo an -
rending! Un - grate - ful, Ah, I
ta! spe - gne - re non pos - so i ri -
her! Day of wrath, oh what will be thy
lei non è com - mos - so, ha di
heav'n with cour - age arm thee, And a -
sf

Lucy.
do - na il pian - to an - cor; vor - rei
strength to do thy will. None to
Alice.
Co - - me ro - sa i - na - ri - di - ta,
Like a rose 'mid tem - pest bend - ing,
Edgar.
cor, sì, t'a - mo an - cor!
love thee, love thee still!
Arthur.
Qual ter - ri - bi - le mo - men - to,
Oh, may heav'n in mer - cy guide us,
Henry.
mor - si! Ah! è mio san - gue, l'ho tra -
end - ing! Ah! day of wrath, what will be thy
Bide-the-Bent.
ti - gre in pet - to il cor.
vert im - pend - ing ill.
Chorus.
Co - - - me
Like a
Co - - me ro - - - sa i -
Like a rose 'mid
Co - - me ro - - - sa i -
Like a rose 'mid
Vln. & Fl.
legg.

pian - ge - re,
coun - sel me,
ah, vor - rei
Love, oh do
el - - la sta fra mor - te e vi - ta,
Pale re - morse thy heart is rend - ing,
Ah! son
Her de -
più for - mar non so pa - ro - le, den - so ve - lo di spa -
In this hour of wrath and an - guish, Tho' af - fliction now be -
di - ta! el - la sta fra morte e vi - ta,
end - ing! Further grief may be im - pend - ing,
Chi per lei non è com - mos - - so,
Oh may heav'n with courage arm thee,
ro - - sa i - na - - ri - di - - ta
rose 'mid the tem - - pest bend - - ing,
na - - ri - di - - ta el - - la
tem - - pest bend - - ing, Pale re -
na - - ri - di - - ta el - - la
tem - - pest bend - - ing, Pale re -
Cl.

affrett.
pian - ge - re e non pos - - - - -
thou with cour-age arm me,
chi per lei non è com - mos - - so,
Oh may heav'n with cour - age arm thee,
vin - to, son com - mos - - so, t'a - mo, in -
spair - ing looks dis - arm me, Ah, faith - less
ven - to par che co - pra i rai del
tide us, Not for ev - - er let us
ah, che spe - gnere non pos - so i ri -
Her de - spair - ing looks a - larm me, New
ha di ti - gre in pet - to il
and a - vert, and a - vert the im -
el - - la sta fra mor - te e vi - ta.
Pale re - morse her heart now is rend - ing.
sta fra mor - te e vi - ta.
morse her heart now is rend - ing.
sta fra mor - te e vi - ta.
morse her heart now is rend - ing.
cresc.

so, m'abban - do - na il pian-to an-cor!
give me strength to do thy will,
fp
p
ha di ti - gre in pet - to il cor. Co - me
And a - vert im-pend - ing ill; Like a
fp
p
gra - ta, t'a - mo an - cor!
maid, I love thee still!
fp
so - le. Co - me
lan - guish. Like a
fp
mor - si del mio cor; ah! è mio
fears my bo - som fill, Ah! day of
fp
cor, il cor!
pend - ing ill!
Chi per
Oh may
Chi per
Oh may
calando

Vor - rei pian - ge - re,
None to coun - sel me,
ro - sa i - na - ri - di - ta el - - la sta fra mor - te e
rose 'mid tem - pest bend - ing, Pale re - morse thy heart is
ro - sa i - na - ri - di - - ta el - la sta fra mor - te e
rose 'mid tem - pest bend - ing, grief and fear thy heart ar
san - gue, l'ho tra - di - ta, el - la sta fra morte e
wrath, what will be thy end - ing, Further grief may be im -
chi per lei non è com
Oh may heav'n with courage
Chi per le - i non è com -
Oh may heav'n now with cour - - age
lei non è com - mos - - so,
heav'n with cour - - age arm thee,
lei non è com - mos - - so,
heav'n with cour - - age arm thee,

affrett.
cresc.
ah! vor-rei pian - ge - re e non pos- - -
Love, oh do thou with cour-age arm
vi - ta; chi per lei non è com -
rend - ing, Oh, may heav'n with cour - age
ah! son vin - to, son com- mos- - so,
Her de - spair - ing looks dis - arm me,
vi - ta, chi per lei non è com- mos - so ha di
rend - ing, Thy despair - ing looks a - larm me, Name - less
vi - ta, ah, che spe - gne- re non
pend - ing, Her de - spair - ing looks a -
mos - so, ha di ti - gre in
arm thee, and a - vert, and a -
mos - so, ha di ti - gre in pet - to il
arm thee, oh, may heav'n with cour - age now
ha di ti- - gre in pet - to il
oh, may heav'n with cour - age now
ha di ti- - gre in pet - to il
oh, may heav'n with cour - age now
cresc.
cresc.

- - - so, m'abban-do - na il pian-to an
me, give me strength to do thy
mos - so, ha di ti-grein pet-to il cor,
arm thee, And a - vert impend-ing ill,
t'a - mo, in - gra - ta, t'a - - mo an -
ah, faith - less maid, I love thee
ti - - grein pet-to il cor,
fears my bo - som fill,
pos - so i ri - mor - si del mio
larm me, New fears my bo - - som
pet - to il cor, il
vert the im - pend - - ing
co - re, in pet - - to il
arm thee, may heav'n a -
co - re, in pet - - to il
arm thee, may heav'n a -
co - re, in pet - - to il
arm thee, may heav'n a -
calando

rall.
cor, il pian - to an - cor, il pian - to
will, Oh love, give me strength, oh help me,
ah! il cor, in pet-to il cor,
and a- - vert im-pending ill
cor, t'a - mo an - cor, sì, sì, t'a-mo an-cor,
still, I love thee still, yes, I love thee still
ha di ti-gre in pet-to il cor, ha di ti-gre in pet-to il cor,
Name-less fears my bo-som fill, name-less fears my bo-som fill,
cor, non pos - so i ri-mor - si del cor,
fill, A name - less fear my bo - som doth fill,
cor, sì, di ti- - gre, sì, il cor,
ill, and a - vert im - pend - ing ill,
cor, in pet - to il cor, il cor,
vert im - pend - ing ill from her,
cor, in pet - to il cor, il cor,
vert im - pend - ing ill from her,
cor, in pet - to il cor, il cor,
vert im - pend - ing ill from her,

ff
an - cor!
oh, love!
ff
il cor!
from her!
a tempo
cresc.
ff
in-gra - ta, t'a-mo an - cor, sì, an - cor!
Un-grate-ful maid, I love, love thee still!
ff
il cor!
ah me!
a tempo
cresc.
ff
ah spe-gner non li pos - so, ahi - mè!
New grief may be im-pend - ing, ah me!
ff
il cor!
from her!
ff
il cor!
from her!
ff
il cor!
from her!
ff
il cor!
from her!
ff
fff

Nº 10. "T'allontana, sciagurato."

Last Scene of Finale II.

Bide-the-Bent
(interrupting them in a tone of authority.)
rall.
rà. Ri - spet - ta - te in me di Di - o la tre - men - da ma - e -
venge. Stay your hands, nor rash - ly dare to take the life by heav'n be -
rall.
p
a tempo
stà. In suo no - me vel co - man - do, de - po
stowed. In the name of law and hon - or, I com
fp
a tempo
f
ne - te l'i - ra e il bran - do. Pa - ce,
mand you sheathe your weap - ons. Ye are
pa - ce, e - gli ab - bor - ri - sce l'o - mi -
neigh - bors, peace be be - tween ye, it is
ci - da, e scrit - to sta: "Chi di
writ - ten up - on the law: "Who the
fp
fp

fer - ro al - trui fe - - ri - sce, pur di
sword lifts a - gainst his brother, by the
(all sheathe their swords.)
fer - ro pe - ri - - rà.„ Pa - ce,
sword shall he be slain." Peace then, I
fp
f
Henry (advancing towards Edgar.)
pa - ce. Scon - si - glia - to!
charge ye. Rash in - trud - er,
Meno mosso.
p
Edgar (haughtily.)
in que - ste por - te chi ti gui - da? La mia sor - te,
say, what de - sign hath brought thee hith - er? Fate so will'd it,
calando
Henry. Edgar.
il mio drit - to. Scia - gu - ra - to! Sì; Lu -
and my purpose _ What, thy purpose? Yes, thy

Bide-the-Bent
(coming between them.)
ci - a la sua fe - de a me giu - rò! Ah! que - sto a -
sis - ter gave to me her plight - ed troth. That vow for
cresc.
p
mor fu - ne - sto ob - bli - a: el - la è d'al - tri.
ev - er now is can - cell'd, She's an - oth - er's.
fp
Edgar.
D'al-tri!
Never!
Poco più Allegro.
Bide-the-Bent
(showing him the contract. Edgar, having read it, fixes his eyes upon Lucy.)
no.
she?
Mi - ra.
Read then.
'Cello
p
Vl.
Ob.
'Cello
Tymp.
Edgar.
Tre - mi...
Trembling,
ti con - fon - di...
and dis - tracted,
ff
Son tue ci - fre? A me ri - spon -
Didst thou sign this? I will be an -

(pointing to the signature.)
di: son tue ci-fre? Ri-spon-di!
swer'd! Is't thy writ-ing? Give an-swer!
Lucy. (her voice sounding like a groan.)
Sì! Ah!
Yes! Ah!
Edgar. (stifling his rage, he gives her his ring.)
Ripren-di il tuo pe-gno, in-fi-do cor... Il mio
Then take back thy tok-en, perfid-ious heart; That I
Allegro vivace.
sf p
cresc.
f
Tromba & Trombone, etc.
Almen... Ed-gar-do! Ed-gar-do!
Ah no! oh Ed-gar! have mer-cy!
dam-mi. Lo ren-di!
gave thee, re-turn it!
ff
(Lucy, in her anguish scarcely knowing what she is doing, takes off her ring, which Edgar snatches from her.)
Più mosso.
Edgar. a piac. (throws it down and stamps on it.)
Hai tra-di-to il cie-lo e a-mor. Ma-le-det-to, ma-le-
Thou'st be-tray'd me 'fore heaven and earth. Mal-e-dic-tion, mal-e-
Ob.
fp
Strings & Fag.

det - to sia li - stan - te che di - te, sì, che di
dic - tion be up - on thee, Curs'd for ev - er be the
f
Tutti
Cl. Cor. & Fag.
f
te mi re - se a - man - te, stir-pe i-ni - qua, abbomi-na-ta, io do-
hour I lov'd and won thee! Hat-ed race, at last I know ye, and will
Fl.
Ob.
Tymp.
ve - a da te fug-gir, ab - bo - mi - na - ta, ma - le - det - ta, io do-
shun ye for-ev-er more, ye hat-ed race, at last I know ye, and will
fp
Lucy.
Ah!
Ah!
ve - a da te fug - gir. Ah! ma di Dio la ma - no i - ra - ta vi di-
shun ye for - ev - er more. E - ter - nal vengeance here I vow ye, and may
Fl. & Cl.
Cor. & Fag.

Edgar.
sper - da
heav - en
Henry.
In - sa - no ar - dir!
Ah, curse no more!
Bide-the-Bent.
In - sa - no ar - dir!
Ah, curse no more!
SOPRANO.
In -
Ah,
TENOR.
In - sa - no ar - dir! in -
Ah, curse no more! Ah,
BASS.
In - sa - no ar - dir! in -
Ah, curse no more! Ah,
Tutti.
f
p
cresc.
E - sci!
Leave us!
E - sci!
Leave us!
Pa - ce!
Si - lence!
sa - no ar - dir! in - sa - no ar - dir!
curse no more! oh, curse no more!
sa - no ar - dir! in - sa - no ar - dir!
curse no more! oh, curse no more!
sa - no ar - dir! in - sa - no ar - dir!
curse no more! oh, curse no more!
ff

Arthur. (to Edgar.)
Vivace. Tutta forza
E - sci, fug - gi,il fu - ror che m'ac-cen - de
Hence, be - gone, ere our fu - ry as-sail thee,
Tutta forza
E - sci, fug - gi,il fu - ror che m'ac-cen - de
Hence, be - gone, ere our fu - ry as-sail thee,
Tutta forza
In - fe - li - ce, t'in-vo - la, t'af-fret - ta,
Hap - less Ed - gar, oh leave us, I pray thee,
Tutta forza
TENOR.
E - sci, fug - gi il fu - ror che n'ac-cen - de
Hence, be - gone, ere our fu - ry as- sail thee,
BASS.
Tutta forza
E - sci, fug - gi il fu - ror che n'ac-cen - de
Hence, be - gone, ere our fu - ry as-sail thee,
Tutti throughout.
Vivace.
so - lo un pun - to i suoi col - pi so-spen - de, ma fra
Threats and de - fi - ance now naught will a - vail thee, Though our
so - lo un pun - to i suoi col - pi so-spen - de, ma fra
Threats and de - fi - ance now naught will a - vail thee, Though our
i tuoi gior - ni il suo sta - to ri-spet - ta, vi - vi e
Let not rash - ly thy fu - ry be-tray thee, Peace will
so - lo un pun - to i suoi col - pi so-spen - de, ma fra
Threats and de - fi - ance now naught will a - vail thee, Though our
so - lo un pun - to i suoi col - pi so-spen - de, ma fra
Threats and de - fi - ance now naught will a - vail thee, Though our

po - co più a - tro - ce, più fie - re sul tu-o ca - po ab-bor-
ven-geance may now be a - vert - ed, Yet, ere long, on thy
po - co più a - tro - ce, più fie - re sul tu-o ca - po ab-bor-
ven-geance may now be a - vert - ed, Yet, ere long, on thy
for - se il tuo duo - lo fia spen - to: tut to è lie - ve al l'e-
come with the dawn of to - mor - row, Let not an - ger thy
po - co più a - tro - ce, più fie - ro sul tu-o ca - po ab-bor-
ven-geance may now be a - vert - ed, Yet, ere long, on thy
po - co più a - tro - ce, più fie - ro sul tu-o ca - po ab-bor-
ven-geance may now be a - vert - ed, Yet, ere long, on thy
ri - to ca - drà, ma fra po - co più a-
head it shall fall, Though our ven - geance may
ri - to ca - drà, ma fra po - co più a-
head it shall fall, Though our ven - geance may
ter - na pie - tà; vi vi e for - se il tuo
rea - son en - thrall, Peace will come with the
ri - to ca - drà, ma fra po - co più a-
head it shall fall, Though our ven - geance may
ri - to ca - drà, ma fra po - co più a-
head it shall fall, Though our ven - geance may

cresc.
ff
tro - ce, più fie - ro sul tu-o ca - po ab-bor-
now be a - vert - ed, Yet, ere long, on thy
duo - lo fia spen - to tut - to è lie - ve al le-
dawn of to - mor - row, Let not an - ger thy
Lucy. (falling on her knees)
Dio, lo sal - va, in sì
Save him, heav'n from de-
Edgar. (throwing away his sword, and offering his breast for them to strike)
Tru - ci - da - te - mi e
Let me die then, for
ri - to ca - drà.
head it shall fall.
ter - na pie - tà.
rea - son en - thrall.
p

fie - ro mo - men - to d'u - na mi - se - ra a
struc - tion and dan - ger, Pour on me all the

pro - nu - bo al ri - to sia - lo scem - pio d'un
glad - ly I per - ish, Since I've lost what on

Bide-the-Bent.

In - fe - li - -
Hap - less Ed - -

Lucy.

scol - ta il la - men - to. È la pre - ce d'im - men - so do -
flood of thy an - ger; Grant the pray'r of a heart that is

Edgar.

co - re tra - di - to. Del mio san - gue co - per - ta la
earth I did cher - ish: Let my life - blood be shed on the

Arthur.

E - sci!
Leave us!

Henry.

E - sci!
Leave us!

Bide-the-Bent.

- - ce!
- - gar!

Chorus.

E - sci!
Leave us!

E - sci!
Leave us!

Lucy.
lo - re, che più in ter - ra spe - ran - za non ha,
bro - ken, Let not blood - shed my sens - es ap - pal,
Edgar.
so - glia, dol - ce vi - sta per l'em - pia sa - rà!
al - tar, I am read - y your vic - tim to fall,
Arthur.
Va!
Go!
Henry.
Va!
Go!
Bide-the-Bent. (to Edgar.)
Deh, ti sal - - - va!
Go, I pray thee!
Va!
Go!
Lucy.
è l'e - stre - ma do - man - da del co - re che sul
Love de - vot - ed, un - dy - ing, un - spo - ken, Binds me
Alice.
(to Edgar.)
In - fe - li - ce!
Hap - less lov - ers!
Edgar.
cal - pe - stan - do l'e - san - gue mi - a spo - glia al - l'al -
From her pur - pose it will not make her fal - ter, She is
Henry.
T'in - vo - la,
Thou trai - tor!
Bide-the-Bent.
Vi - vi, for - se il tuo duo - lo, il tuo
Peace will come with dawn to - mor - row, Peace will

Lucy.
lab - bro spi - ran - do mi sta, è l'e - stre - ma do -
to him be - yond re - call, Grant the pray'r of a
Alice.
t'in - vo - la, t'af - fret - ta!
Oh leave us, I pray thee!
Edgar.
ta - re più lie - ta ne an - drà, cal - pe - stan - do l'e -
lost to my heart past re - call, Let my life - blood be
Arthur.
Va col san -
Yes, ere long
Henry.
va, va, la mac -
The maid - en's heart
Bide-the-Bent.
duo - lo fi - a spen - to, tut - to è lie - ve,
come with dawn to - mor - row, let not an - ger,
Va, col san -
Yes, ere long
Chorus.
Va, col san -
Yes, ere long
ff

f
man-da d'un co - re che spi-ran-do sul lab-bro mi sta,
heart that is bro - ken, Let not blood-shed my sens-es ap-pal,
f
Ah!
Ah!
f
san-gue mia spo - glia al - l'al-ta - re più lie - ta ne an-drà,
shed on the al - tar, I am read - y your vic - tim to fall,
gue tuo la - - va - - ta sa-rà,
our ven - geance on thee shall fall;
f
chia d'ol-trag - gio sì ne - ro, ah!
thou a - lone hast per-vert - ed, We
f
tut - to è lie - ve al - l'e - ter - na pie - tà,
let not an - ger then thy rea - son en - thral,
gue tuo la - va - ta sa - rà,
our ven - geance on thee shall fall,
gue tuo la - va - ta sa - rà,
our ven - geance on thee shall fall,
ff

che - spi - ran - do sul lab - bro mi sta,
Let not blood - shed my sens - es ap - pal,
il suo sta - to, i suoi gior - ni ri - spet - ta, ah,
Let not rash - ly thy fu - ry be - tray thee, ah,
al - l'al - ta - re più lie - ta ne an - drà, lie -
I am read - y your vic - tim to fall, your
sì, sì, sa - - - rà, va
it soon shall fall, go,
la - - va - - ta col san - - -
have doom'd thee to per - - -
tut - to e lie - ve, tut - - - to, al -
let not an - ger, an - - - ger thus
sì, sì, sa - - - rà,
it soon shall fall,
sì, sì, sa - - - rà,
it soon shall fall,
p

ff
sul lab - - bro mi sta, mi
my sens - - es ap - pal, oh
va, va,
be - - - gone,
- ta ne an -
vic - - - tim to
va, va.
trai - - - tor!
gue la - va - - - ta sa -
ish be - yond all re -
- l'e - ter - - - na pie -
thy rea - - - son en -
va, va!
go, go!
va, va!
go, go!

Più Allegro.
sta.
heav'n.
Dio,
Save
va! In - fe - li - - - ce, t'in - vo - la, t'af - fret - -
go, hap-less Ed - - - gar, oh leave us, I pray
drà.
fall.
No,
Strike,
E - -
Fly
rà.
call.
E - -
Fly
tà.
thral.
Ah, vi - - - vi, e for - -
Ah go, hap - less Ed - -
SOPRANOS.
In - - - fe - - - li - - - ce, t'in - vo - -
Hap - - less Ed - - gar, oh leave
E - -
Fly
E - -
Fly
Più Allegro.
ff

lo sal - - - va!
him, save him!
- - - - ta, i tuoi gior - - ni, il suo
thee, Let not rash - - ly thy
no, no tru-ci - da-te-mi.
strike, I'll be your vic - tim.
sci, fug - - - gi!
then, leave us.
sci, fug - - - gi!
then, leave us.
se il tuo duo - lo fia spen - - to, tut -
gar, peace will come with to mor - - row. Ah!
la, t'af - fret - ta, i tuoi gior -
us, we pray thee, Let not rash -
sci, fug - - - gi,
then, leave us,
sci, fug - - - gi,
then, leave
ff

In sì fie - - ro mo - men - to,
Pour on me all thy an - ger,
sta - to ri - spet - - - - ta, vi - vi, e
fu - ry be - tray thee, Peace will
No, no, no, no, cal - pe - sta te - mi, sì,
Yes, let my blood flow up - on the al - tar,
il fu - ror che m'ac - cen - de
We have doom'd thee to per - ish,
fug - gi, van - - - ne,
Hear, or per - - - ish,
to è lie - ve all'e - ter - na pie - tà, sì,
let not an - ger thus thy rea - son en - thral, have
ni, il suo sta - to ri - spet - ta. Ah,
ly thy an - ger be - tray thee, have
il fu - ror che n'ac - cen - de,
We have doom'd thee to per - ish,
il fu - ror che n'ac - cen - de,
We have doom'd thee to per - ish,

ah d'u - na mi - se-ra a-scol - ta l'ac-cen - to, Dio, lo
Ah, grant the pray'r of a heart that is brok - en, heav'n, oh
for - se il tuo duo - lo fia spen - to, tut - to è lie - - ve al - l'e -
come with the dawn of to - mor - row, Let not an - - ger thy
del mio san - gue co - per - ta la so - glia, la so -
From her pur - pose 'twill not make her fal - ter, I've lost
so - lo un pun - to i suoi col - pi so - spen -
Thou, yes, thou the maid - en's heart hast per - vert -
la mac - chia la - va - ta col san - gue sa -
We've doom'd thee to per - ish be - yond all re -
tut - to sì, tut - to, sì, tut - to, al - l'e-
pa - tience, have pa - tience, have pa - tience, time has
vi - vi, e for - se il tuo duo - lo fia
pa - tience, have pa - tience, let not an - ger thy
so - lo un pun - to i suoi col - pi so - spen -
Thou, yes, thou the maid - en's heart hast per - vert -
so - lo un pun - to i suoi col - pi so - spen -
Thou, yes, thou the maid - en's heart hast per - vert -

sal - va, Di - o, Di - o,
save him, save him, save him,
ter - na pie - tà, ah, sì, ah, sì,
rea-son en-thral, Ah, no, Ah, no,
- - glia dol - ce vi - sta sa - - rà,
her, Ah, for ev - er lost her,
- - de, sì, sì, sì, sì,
- - ed, Ah, yes, ah, yes,
rà, la-va - ta col san - gue, lavata sa-rà, sì,
call, we've doom'd thee to per - ish beyond all recall, yes,
ter - na pie - tà, tut - to, sì, sì,
sol-ace for all, pa - tience, pa - tience,
spen - to, ah! sì, Ah! sì,
rea - son en - thral, Ah, no!
- - de, sì, sì, sì, sì,
- - ed, Ah, yes, Ah, yes,
- - de, sì, sì, sì, sì,
- - ed, Ah, yes, Ah, yes,

è l'e - stre - ma,
Love de - vot - ed,
Di -
leave
tru - ci - da - te,
let me per - ish,
e - sci fug - gi, il fu - ror che m'ac - cen - de so - lo un
Hence, be - gone, ere our fu - ry as - sail thee, Threats and de -
e - sci, fug - gi, il fu - ror che m'ac - cen - de so - lo un
Hence, be - gone, ere our fu - ry as - sail thee, Threats and de -
in - fe - li - ce, t'in - vo - la, t'af - fret - ta, i tuo - i
Hap - less Ed - gar, oh leave us, I pray thee, Let not
fug - gi,
Fly then,
e - sci, fug - gi, il fu - ror che n'ac - cen - de so - lo un
Hence, be - gone, ere our fu - ry as - sail thee, Threats and de -
e - sci, fug - gi, il fu - ror che n'ac - cen - de so - lo un
Hence, be - gone, ere our fu - ry as - sail thee, Threats and de -

cresc.
l'e - stre - ma do - man - da che sul - lab - bro mi
un - dy - ing, un - spo - ken, Binds me to him past re -
o! Di - o! fug - gi,
us! leave us! fly then,
tru - ci - da - te, cal - pe - sta - te, cal - pe -
Let me per - ish, strike, and spare not, strike, and
pun - to i suoi col - pi so - spen - de, ma fra po - co più a - tro - ce, più
fi - ance no more will a - vail thee, Though our vengeance may now be a -
pun - to i suoi col - pi so - spen - de, ma fra po - co più a - tro - ce, più
fi - ance no more will a - vail thee, Though our vengeance may now be a -
gior - ni, il suo sta - to ri - spet - ta, vi - vi, e for - se il tuo duo - lo fia
rash - ly thy fu - ry be - tray thee, Peace will come with the dawn of to -
e - sci, e - sci,
leave us, fly then,
pun - to i suoi col - pi so - spen - de, ma fra po - co più a - tro - ce, più
fi - ance no more will a - vail thee, Though our vengeance may now be a -
pun - to i suoi col - pi so - spen - de, ma fra po - co più a - tro - ce, più
fi - ance no more will a - vail thee, Though our vengeance may now be a -

sta, Ah, sì, che
call, Ah, yes, binds
tut - to è lie-ve al-l'e - ter - na pie - tà, al - l'
Let not an-ger thy rea - son en - thral, not
sta - - - - - - - - - te, al l'
spare not, She
fie - ro sul tuo ca-po ab-bor-ri - to ca - drà, sul tuo
vert - ed, yet, ere long, on thy head it shall fall, Yes, ere
fie - ro sul tuo ca-po ab-bor-ri - to ca - drà, sul tuo
vert - ed, yet, ere long, on thy head it shall fall, Yes, ere
spen - to, tut - to è lie-ve al-l'e - ter - na pie - tà, tut - to
mor - row, Let not an - ger thy rea - son en - thral, Let not
tut - to è lie-ve al-l'e - ter - na pie - tà, tut - to
Let not an - ger thy rea - son en - thral, Let not
fie - ro, sul tuo ca - po ab-bor - ri - to ca - drà, sul tuo
ver - ted, yet, ere long, on thy head it shall fall, Yes, ere
fie - ro, sul tuo ca - po ab-bor - ri - to ca - drà, sul tuo
ver - ted, yet, ere long, on thy head it shall fall, Yes, ere
ff

lab - - bro mi sta, sul lab - bro mi
to him past re - call, to him past re -
ter - - na pie - tà, al - l'e - ter - - na pie -
rea - - son en - thral, not thy rea - - son en -
ta - re più lie - ta ne an-drà, più lie - - ta ne an -
lost to thy heart past re - call, she's lost past all re -
ca - po ab-bor-ri - to ca - drà, sì, sul tu-o ca - - po ca -
long on thy head it shall fall, yes, yes, on thy head it shall
ca - po ab-bor-ri - to ca - drà, sì, sul tu-o ca - - po ca -
long on thy head it shall fall, yes, yes, on thy head it shall
lie - ve al-l'e - ter - na pie - tà, sì, tut - to è lie - - -
an - ger thy rea - son en - thral, thy rea - son en - thral,
lie - ve al-l'e - ter - na pie - tà, sì, al - l'e - ter - na pie -
an - ger thy rea - son en - thral, no, not thy rea - - son en -
ca - po ab-bor - ri - to ca - drà, sì, sul tu-o ca - - po ca -
long on thy head it shall fall, yes, yes on thy head it shall
ca - po ab-bor - ri - to ca - drà, sì, sul tu-o ca - - po ca -
long on thy head it shall fall, yes, yes on thy head it shall

Più allegro.
sta, sì, è l'e - stre - ma do - man - da del co - re che spi -
call, yes, love de - vot - ed, un - dy - ing, un - spo - ken, binds me,
tà, sì, quan - te vol - te ad un so - lo tor - men - to mil - le
thral, ah, heav'n - ly love hath a balm for thy sor - row, Time hath
drà, sì, cal - pe - stan - do l'e - san - gue mia spo - glia, sì, più
call, ah, let my life - blood be shed on the al - tar, She is
drà, sì, sì, la mac - chia d'ol - trag - gio sì ne - ro col tuo
fall, The maid - en's heart hath by thee been per - vert - ed, Thou art
drà, sì, sì, la mac - chia d'ol - trag - gio sì ne - ro col tuo
fall, The maid - en's heart hath by thee been per - vert - ed, We have
ve, sì, quan - te vol - te ad un so - lo tor - men - to,
heav'n - ly love hath balm, it hath balm for thy sor - row,
tà, sì, quan - te vol - te ad un so - lo tor - men - to
thral, ah, heav'n - ly love hath a balm for thy sor - row,
drà, sì, sì, la mac - chia d'ol - trag - gio sì ne - ro
fall, the maid - en's heart hath by thee been per - vert - ed,
drà, sì, sì, la mac - chia d'ol - trag - gio sì ne - ro col tuo
fall, the maid - en's heart hath by thee been per - vert - ed, We have
Più allegro.

ran - - do mi sta, sì, è l'e - stre- ma do - man - da del
binds me to him, yes, love de - vot - ed, un - dy - ing, un-
gio - je appre - sta - te non ha, sì, quan - te vol - te ad un so - lo tor-
sol- ace and com-fort for all, Yes, heav'n - ly love hath a balm for thy
lie - - ta n'an - drà, sì, cal - pe - stan - do l'e - san - gue mia
lost past re - call, ah, let my life-blood be shed on the
san - gue la - va - ta sa - rà, sì, col tuo san - gue la - va - ta sa-
doom'd thee, be-yond all re-call, yes, we have doom'd thee be - yond all re-
san - gue la - va - ta sa - rà, sì, col tuo san - gue la - va - ta sa-
doom'd thee, be-yond all re-call, yes, we have doom'd thee be - yond all re-
gio - je ap-pre - sta - te non ha, sì, quan-te vol - te ad un so - lo tor-
Time hath a sol- ace for all, yes, heav'n-ly love hath a balm for thy
mil - le gio - - je, sì, quan - te vol - te ad un so - lo tor-
Then have pa - - tience, yes, heav'n - ly love hath a balm for thy
la - - va - ta sa - rà, sì, col tuo san - gue la - va - ta sa-
Thou'rt doom'd past re - call, yes, we have doom'd thee be - yond all re-
san - gue la - va - ta sa - rà, sì, col tuo san - gue la - va - ta sa-
doom'd thee be-yond all re - call, yes, we have doom'd thee be - yond all re-
tr
tr
tr

co - - - - - - re
spo - - - - - - ken,
men-to quan-te gio - je, ah!
sor - row, Time hath sol - ace, ah!
spo - glia, al - l'al - ta - - -
al - tar, she is lost,
rà, col tuo
call. We have
rà, sì, col tuo san - gue la - va - - ta sa-
call. Yes, we have doom'd thee be - yond all re-
p
men-to, ad un sol, quan - te gio - - je ap - pre -
sor - row, Time hath sol - - - ace, hath sol - - ace and
men - to mil - - le
sor - row, pa - - tience,
rà, col tuo
call. Fly then,
rà, col tuo
call. Fly then,
p
p

che mo - - ren - do sul lab - - -
binds me to him be - yond
quan - - te, quan - - te gio - - je ap - pre -
time hath sol - - ace, sol - - ace and
re più lie - - ta, più lie - - -
she is lost to my heart
san - - gue, sol col tuo san - - gue la -
doom'd thee, Yes, we have doom'd thee be -
rà, sì, sol col tuo san - - gue la -
call, we've doom'd thee to per - - ish be -
sta - te, sì, ap - - pre - sta - - -
com - fort, sol - - ace and com - - -
ap - - pre -
Heav'n hath
san - - gue la -
Thou'rt doom'd be -
san - - gue la -
Thou'rt doom'd be -
ff
f

bro mi sta, sul lab - bro mi
all re - call, be - yond all re -
sta - te non ha, ap - pre - sta - te non
com - fort for all, Heav'n - ly love hath a
ta ne an - drà, più lie - ta ne an -
past re - call, she's lost past re -
va - ta sa - rà, la - va - ta sa -
yond all re - call, be - yond all re -
va - ta sa - rà, la - va - ta sa -
yond all re - call, be - yond all re -
te non ha, ap - pre - sta - te non
fort for all, time hath com - fort for
sta - te non ha, ap - pre sta - te non
sol - ace for all, heav'n hath sol - ace for
va - ta sa - rà, la - va - ta sa -
yond all re - call, be - yond all re -
va - ta sa - rà, la - va - ta sa -
yond all re - call, be - yond all re -

sta, sul lab - bro mi sta, sì,
call, be - yond all re - call, be -
ha, ap - pre - sta - te non ha! E -
balm, heav'n - ly love hath a balm. Fly
drà, più lie - ta ne an - drà, sì,
call, she's lost past re - call, ah
rà, la - va - ta sa - rà! E -
call, be - yond all re - call. Fly
rà, la - va - ta sa - rà! E -
call, be - yond all re - call. Fly
ha, ap - pre - sta - te non ha! E -
all, time hath com - fort for all. Fly
ha, ap - pre - sta - te non ha, ah
all, heav'n hath sol - ace for all. for
rà, la - va - ta sa - rà! E -
call, be - yond all re - call. Fly
rà, la - va - ta sa - rà! E -
call, be - yond all re - call. Fly

sì, mi sta, ahi - - - -
yond re - - call, ah
sci, fug - - gi, sì, tut - to è lie - ve al - l'e - ter - na pie -
then, fly then, let not thy an - ger thy rea - son en -
sì, ne an - - drà, sì, sì, più lie - ta ne an -
yes, she's lost, for ev - er - more, to me she's
sci, fug - - gi, o col tuo san - gue la - va - ta sa -
then, trai - - tor, for we have doom'd thee be - yond all re -
sci, fug - - gi, o col tuo san - gue la - va - ta sa -
then, trai - - tor, for we have doom'd thee be - yond all re -
sci, fug - - gi, sì, tut - to è lie - ve al - l'e - ter - na pie -
then, fly then, be - ware, lest thy an - ger thy rea - son en -
sì, non ha, sì, quan - te gio - je ap - pre - sta - te non
all, for all, yes, heav'n hath sol - ace and com - fort for
sci, fug - - gi, o col tuo san - gue la - va - ta sa -
then, trai - - tor, for we have doom'd thee be - yond all re -
sci, fug - - gi, o col tuo san - gue la - va - ta sa -
then, trai - - tor, for we have doom'd thee be - yond all re -

mè!
me!
tà.
thral!
drà.
lost.
rà.
call.
rà.
call.
tà.
thral.
ha!
all.
rà.
call.
rà.
call.

End of Act II.

Act III.

Nº 11. "Qui del padre ancor respira."

Storm, Recitative and Duet.

Hall in the Castle of Ravenswood; a rude table and an old arm-chair are the only furniture. At the back a practicable door and an open casement. It is night, and a storm is raging. Edgar is seated by the table, plunged in thought; after a few moments he rises, goes to the window and looks out.

Vln. & Ob.
Fl. & Cl.
Fag.
rall. un poco
p
p
p

Allegro.
cresc.
f

Edgar. Recit.
Allegro vivace.

Or - ri-da è que-sta not-te co-me il de-sti - no mi - o!
Dark is the night, and stormy, like to my ad - verse for-tune!

(Thunder is heard.)
p
Tymp.

ff

Recit.

Sì, tuo-na, o cie - lo im-per-ver-sa - te, o
Flash, oh ye lightnings, burst forth a-new, ye

f

ful-mi-ni_ scon-vol-to sia l'or-din di na - tu-ra_ e pe-ra il
thun-der-bolts, thou tempest, convulse the heart of na-ture, let all things
Allegro.
mon - do! Ma non m'in-gan-no!
per - ish. But what ap-proaches?
Fl.
Viola, Fag. & 'Cello.
cresc.
Scal-pi-tar d'ap-pres-so o - do un de-strier! S'ar-
Do my ears de-ceive me? Hoofs sound be-low! A-
rinf.
Recit.
resta! Chi mai del-la tem-pe-sta fra le mi-nac-ce e l'i-ra, chi puo te a me ve-
light-ing, who comes in night and darkness, a-mid the rag-ing tempest, to this desert-ed
Allegro.
Henry. (throwing off his cloak.)
Edgar.
ni-re?
mansion?
I - o! Qua-le ar-
See me! What hath

Andante.
Henry.
di - re!
brought thee?
Asthon!
Ashton!
Sì!
Ay!
ff
p Strings.
Edgar.
Fra que - ste mu - ra o - si of - frir - ti al mio co -
Thou dar'st to brave me, whom thy treacher - ous arts have
Fag. sustain.
Tymp.
Henry.
Edgar.
spet - to! Io vi sto per tua scia - gu - ra. Per
blight - ed? I have come t'avenge my hon - or. Thy
Tutti.
ff
Henry.
Moderato.
mi - a? Non ve - ni - sti nel mio tet - to?
hon - or? Yes I've vow'd I will chas - tise thee.
Brass.
f
p
Strings.
Edgar
Qui del
Here a-
pp
Strings.

pa - dre an-cor — re - spi - ra l'om-bra i - nul - ta,e par che
veng - ing shades sur - round thee Of thy vic - tims,slain by
Cor.
fre - ma! mor-te o-gn'au - ra a te — qui— spi - ra! il ter-
trea - son! Oh be-ware, lest they— con - found thee, Thou art
f
f
ren, il ter-ren per te qui tre - ma! Nel var-car la so - glia or-
come, thou art come in e-vil sea - son! Still my race thou per - se-
Cl.
affrett. un
ren - da ben do-vre - sti pal - pi - tar, co-me un
cut - est, E'er by wrath - ful pas - sion led, Now my
poco
a tempo
uom — che — vi - vo — scen - da la sua tom - ba ad al-ber-
thresh - old — thou — pol - lut - est, Be my ven - geance on thy
affrett.
ff a tempo

tratt.
gar, nel var-car la so-glia or - ren da, nel var-car la so-glia or-
head; Still my race thou per-se - cut-est, still my race thou per - se-
Vln. Ob. & Cl.
p tratt. colla parte
ren - da ben do - vre - sti pal - pi - tar, co - me un uom che vi - vo
cut - est, By thy wrath-ful pas-sions led, Now my thresh-old thou pol -
ff
p cresc.
scen-da, co - me un uom che vi - vo scen-da la sua tom - ba ad al - ber -
lut - est, now my threshold thou pol - lut - est, Be my ven-geance on thy
gar, ad al - ber - gar, ad al - ber - gar, la sua tom - ba, la sua
head, yes, be my ven-geance on thy head, be my ven-geance, be my
affrett.
cresc.
a tempo
Henry. (with savage joy.)
tom - - ba ad al - - ber - gar! Fu con-
ven - - geance up - on thy head. I am
ff
a tempo
p

dot - ta al sa - cro ri-to quin - di al ta - la - mo Lu-
come to bear thee tidings that the mar - riage is ac-
Edgar.
ci - a. (Ei più squar - cia il cor fe - ri - to! Oh tor-
complished. (Oh, my heart will rend a - sun - der! Oh dis-
men - to! oh ge-lo - si - a! oh ge - lo-
trac - tion, oh cru-el for - tune! Thought of dis-
Henry.
El - la è al ta - la - mo.
Hand and heart she gave
ff
si - a!)
trac-tion!)
ff
Eb - ben? eb - ben?
What wilt thou here?
p
f
Henry.
A-
I'll
pp
scol-ta!
tell thee.
Di le - ti - zia il mio sog - gior - no e di
While my cas - tle's walls re - sound - ed With the

plau - si rim - bom - ba - va; ma più for - te al cor d'in -
tones of mirth and glad - ness, From my heart all joy re -
f
ter-no la ven - det - ta, la ven-det - ta mi par - la - va! Qui mi
bounded, For the thought of thee, the thought of thee was mad - ness! Mor-tal
p
tras - si, in mez - zo ai ven - ti, la sua vo - ce u - dia tut -
ha - tred I have sworn thee, From my fu - ry naught can
affrett.
Tempo I.
tor, e il fu - ror de - gl'e - le - men - ti ri - spon -
save, I'll chas - tise thee, as I scorn thee, And my
affrett.
ff a tempo
tratt. e rall.
de - va al mio fu - ror, il fu - ror de - gli e - le - men - ti, il fu - ror de - gli e - le -
scorn thou shalt not brave; I'll chastise thee, as I scorn thee, I'll chastise thee, as I
p colla parte

(Oh tor - men - to, oh ge - lo -
(Oh, my heart will rend a -
men - ti ri - spon - de - va al mio fu - ror, il fu - ror de - gli e - le -
scorn thee, And my scorn thou shalt not brave, I'll chas - tise thee, as I
ff p cresc.
si - a!)
sun - der!)
men - ti, il fu - ror de - gli e - le - men - ti ri - spon - de - va al mio fu -
scorn thee, I'll chas - tise thee, as I scorn thee, and my scorn thou shalt not
ror, al mio fu - ror, al mio fu - ror, il fu - ror de - gli e - le -
brave, no, no, my scorn thou shalt not brave, I'll chastise thee, as I
affrett.
cresc.
Edgar (with haughty impa tience.)
men - ti ri - spon - de - va, ri - spon - de - va al mio fu - ror! Da me che
scorn thee, and my scorn, ah, no, my scorn thou shalt not brave! What dost tho
ff
f

Henry.
bra - mi? A - scol - ta - mi!
seek here? To chal - lenge thee!
ff
p
f
On - de pu - nir l'of - fe - sa,
Yes, I to death de - fy thee:
pp
de' mie - i, de' mie - i, la spa - da
De - struc - tion, de - struc - tion I have
vin - di - ci pen - de su te so - spe - sa, on - de pu - nir l'of -
sworn to thee, Come, to the com - bat fly we, I to the death de -
fe - sa, ma ch'al - tri ti spen - ga, ma - i -
fy thee, None now shall take vengeance on thee,
fz

Edgar.
a tempo
rall.
So che al pa-ter-no ce-ne-re giu-rai strap-par-ti al
Know then, that by my father's tomb to thee I've sworn de-
chi dee sve-nar-ti il sa-i!
None but my-self who have doom'd thee!
a tempo
Allegro.
Edgar (with lofty disdain.)
co-re. Sì.
struc-tion. Ay! We
Allegro.
Tu!— Thou!
Tu! Thou!
Henry. Meno.
Quan-do? Al pri-mo sor-ge-re del mat-tu-ti-no al-
meet, then? I'll meet thee when to-mor-row's dawn be-gins to
Tempo I. Edgar. Henry.
bo-re. O-ve? Fra l'ur-ne ge-li-de
bright-en. Where? Near to the mould'ring tombs
Edgar.
di Ravenswood. Ver-rò. Sì, ver-
of Ravenswood. 'Tis well. Yes, I'll

rò, sì! sì!
meet thee there!
Henry.
a piacere
I - vi_a re - star pre - pa - ra - ti.
Soon shall that tomb close o - ver thee.
f colla parte
Maestoso
(oppure)
I - vi t'uc - ci - de - rò.
Boast - er! there thou shalt die.
Al pri - mo_al -
At dawn to -
Al pri - mo_al - bo - re.
At dawn to - mor - row.
f
bo - re. Ah! O
mor - row. Ah! The
Marziale.
so - le più rat - to a
day of my ven - geance no
Ah! O so - le più rat - to a
Ah! The day of my ven - geance no
Marziale.
Strings pizz. Cl. and Brass.
fp
sor - ger t'ap - pre - sta, ti cin - ga di san - gue, ghir -
lon - ger shall tar - ry, Nor swift ret - ri - bu - tion a -
sor - ger t'ap - pre - sta, ti cin - ga di san - gue, ghir -
lon - ger shall tar - ry, Nor swift ret - ri - bu - tion a -
fp

lan-da fu - ne-sta, con quel-la ri - schia-ra l'or - ri - bi - le
gain thou shalt par-ry, The morning that dooms thee, the grave that en -
lan-da fu - ne-sta, con quel-la ri - schia-ra l'or - ri - bi - le
gain thou shalt par-ry, The morning that dooms thee, the grave that en -
sempre stacc.
rall.
ga - ra d'un o - dio mor - ta - le, d'un cie - co fu - ro - re, o
tombs thee No earth-ly re - sis-tance can lon - ger a - vert. The
rall.
ga - ra d'un o - dio mor - ta - le, d'un cie - co fu - ro - re, o
tombs thee No earth-ly re - sis-tance can lon - ger a - vert. The
Ob.
f p
rall.
a tempo
affrett.
so - le più rat - to ri - sor - gi e ri - schia - ra d'un o - dio mor -
day of my ven - geance no lon - ger shall tar - ry, No earthly re -
a tempo
affrett.
so - le più rat - to ri - sor - gi e ri - schia - ra d'un
day of my ven - geance no lon - ger shall tar - ry, No
Tutti
f a tempo
affrett.
ta - le il cie - co, il cie - co fu -
sis - tance thy doom now can lon - ger a -
o - dio mor - ta - le il cie - co, il cie - co fu -
earth - ly re - sis - tance thy doom now can lon - ger a -
ff
14047

ror.
vert.
Giu - ra - i strap - -
Ah, yes, to thee I've
ror.
vert.
par - ti il co - - re.
sworn de - struc - - tion.
La
'Tis
Fra
Meet
spa - - da pen - de su te.
I who have doom'd thee to die.
l'ur - ne di Ravens-wood
me at morn by the tomb.
Al - - l'al ba ver - -
I'll meet thee, be

Ah! Fa-rà di nostr' al-me a-tro-ce go-
Ah! En-san-guined and lu-rid the day is a-
rò. Ah! Fa-rà di nostr' al-me a-tro-ce go-
sure. Ah! En-san-guined and lu-rid the day is a-
fp
ver-no gri-dan-do ven-det-ta lo spir-to d'A-ver-no. del
ris-ing, When ha-tred and fu-ry no more need dis-guising, 'Mid
ver-no gri-dan-do ven-det-ta lo spir-to d'A-ver-no. del
ris-ing, When ha-tred and fu-ry no more need dis-guising, 'Mid
fp
(The storm is at its height.)
tuo-no che mug-ge, del nem-bo che rug-ge, più
lightning and thunder I'd rend thee a-sun-der, Though
tuo-no che mug-ge, del nem-bo che rug-ge, più
lightning and thunder I'd rend thee a-sun-der, Though
pp
sempre stacc.
l'i-ra è tre-men-da che m'ar-de nel co-re. O
de-mons of e-vil would shield thee from harm. The
l'i-ra è tre-men-da che m'ar-de nel co-re. O
de-mons of e-vil would shield thee from harm. The
p

affrett.
so - - le, più rat - to ri - sor-gi e ri - schia-ra d'un o - dio mor -
day of my vengeance no longer shall tar - ry, No earth - ly re -
so - - le, più rat - to ri - sor-gi e ri - schia-ra d'un
day of my vengeance no longer shall tar - ry, No
f
affrett.
ta - - - - le il cie - co, il cie - co fu -
sist - - - - ance thy doom now can longer a -
o - dio mor - ta - - le il cie - co, il cie - co fu -
earth - ly re - sist - ance thy doom now can longer a -
Più Allegro.
ror, l'or - ri - bi - le ga - ra d'un o - dio mor -
vert. The grave that en - tombs thee, No mor - tal re -
ror, con quel - la ri - schia - ra d'un o - dio mor -
vert. The morn-ing that dooms thee, No mor - tal re -
Più Allegro.
ta - le, d'un cie - co fu - ror, d'un cie - co fu - ror, d'un
sistance can long-er a - vert, no, naught now can long, can
ta - le, d'un cie - co fu - ror, d'un cie - co fu - ror, d'un
sistance can long-er a - vert, no, naught now can long, can
f

cie - co fu - ror, d'un cie - co fu - ror, d'un
long - er a - vert, no, naught can a - vert, no,
cie - co fu - ror, d'un cie - co fu - ror, d'un
long - er a - vert, no, naught can a - vert, no,
cie - co fu - ror, d'un cie - co fu - ror, d'un cie - co fu - ror, d'un cie - co fu -
naught can a - vert, no, naught can a - vert, no, naught can a - vert, no, naught can a -
cie - co fu - ror, d'un cie - co fu - ror, d'un cie - co fu - ror, d'un cie - co fu -
naught can a - vert, no, naught can a - vert, no, naught can a - vert, no, naught can a -
(Exeunt.)
ror!
vert!
ror!
vert!

Nº 12. "D'immenso giubilo."

Chorus.

A hall at Sir Henry Ashton's, as in Act I. From the neighboring rooms dance-music is heard. At the back of the Stage are the guests and inmates of the castle, who converse in groups.

SOPRANOS.
TENORS.
BASS.
Chorus.
D'im - men - so giu - bi - lo s'in - nal - zi un gri - do.
With war - like min - strel - sy raise loud your voic - es,
D'im - men - so giu - bi - lo s'in - nalzi un gri - do:
With war - like minstrel - sy raise loud your voic - es,
cor - ra la Scozia di li - do in
Now ev - 'ry Scottish heart once more re -
f
p

li - do, e av - ver-ta i per - fi - di no - stri ne - mi - ci,
joic - es, Sound it from ev - 'ry lip, fall'n is the foe - man;
che a noi sor - ri - do - no le stelle an - cor, e av - verta i
Fate smiles up - on us, and strife is no more; Sound it from
cresc.
per - fi - di no - stri ne - mi - ci, che a noi sor - ri - do - no le
ev - 'ry lip, fall'n is the foe - man, Fate smiles up - on us now, And

stel - le an - cor.
strife is no more.
stel - le an - cor.
strife is no more.
stel - le an - cor.
strife is no more.
Str.
pp
p
BASS.
Che più ter - ri - bi - li, che più fe - li - ci, ne ren - de
Rest now, ye war - riors, Sing it, oh wom - en, Let it re -
d'al - to fa - vor, d'al - to fa -
from shore to shore, from shore to
d'al - to fa - vor, d'al - to fa -
from shore to shore, from shore to
l'au - ra d'al - to fa - vor, d'al - to fa - vor, d'al - to fa -
sound from shore to shore, from shore to shore, from shore to
ff

vor, e av - ver - ta i per - fi - di no - stri ne - mi - ci, che a
shore, Sound it from ev - 'ry lip, fall'n is the foe - man, Fate
vor, e av - ver - ta i per - fi - di no - stri ne - mi - ci, che a
shore, Sound it from ev - 'ry lip, fall'n is the foe - man, Fate
vor, e av - ver - ta i per - fi - di no - stri ne - mi - ci, che a
shore, Sound it from ev - 'ry lip, fall'n is the foe - man, Fate
f
cresc.
noi sor - ri - di - no le stel - le an - cor, av - ver - ta i
smiles up - on us now, And strife is no more; Sound it from
noi sor - ri - di - no le stel - le an - cor, av - ver - ta i
smiles up - on us now, And strife is no more; Sound it from
noi sor - ri - di - no le stel - le an - cor, av - ver - ta i
smiles up - on us now, And strife is no more; Sound it from
f
ff
per - fi - di no - stri ne - mi - ci, che a
ev - 'ry lip, Fate smiles up - on us, Fate
per - fi - di no - stri ne - mi - ci, che a
ev - 'ry lip, Fate smiles up - on us, Fate
per - fi - di no - stri ne - mi - ci, che a
ev - 'ry lip, Fate smiles up - on us, Fate
ff

noi sor - ri - - do - no le
smiles up - on us now, And
stel - - le, le stel - le an - cor, le
strife is no more, is no more, strife
stel - le an - cor, le stel - le an - cor!
is no more, strife is no more!

Nº 13. "Dalle stanze, ove Lucia."

Recit. and Chorus.

Maestoso. (making signs that all are to gather round him.)

Ah! Dal - le
Ah! From the

ghiac - ci di ter - ror!
is't? what hath be - fall'n?

ghiac - ci di ter - ror!
is't? what hath be - fall'n?

ghiac - ci di ter - ror!
is't? what hath be - fall'n?

Maestoso.
Cor. & Fag. sustain.

stan - ze, o - ve Lu - ci - a trat - ta a - vea col suo con
cham - ber, where sad and si - lent, To her lord I Lu - cy

sor - - te, un la - men - to - un gri - do u - sci - a, co - me
guid - - ed, Cries of an - guish broke loud up - on us, 'Twixt sur

d'uom vi - ci - no a mor - - te! Cor - si' rat - to in quel - le
prise and fear sore di - vid - - ed, Ter - ror seiz'd me, I burst u

Fl.

Tymp.

rall.
mu - ra— ahi! ter - ri - bi - le scia - gu - ra! Ste - so Ar -
on them, Sight of dread appall'd my— sens - es, By her
Cl. and Fl.
pp
tu - ro al suol gia - ce - va mu - to, fred - do, in - san - gui -
hus - band the bride was kneel - ing, He lay life - less, his wounds con -
Poco più
na - to!— e Lu - cia l'ac - ciar strin - ge - va, che fu già del tru - ci -
geal - ing, In her hand she held the dag - ger, and her an - guish re - com -
Fl.
Tempo I.
da - to! El - la in me le lu - ci af - fis - se— "Il mio
menc - es. Wretched maid, she'd slain her hus - band! Gaz - ing
Tutti.
f
spo - so, ov' è?,, mi dis - se, e nel vol - to suo pal -
on me with eyes all va - cant, She be - lieved 'twas Ed - gar
Hn. sustain
p
Fag.
fp
p

len - - te un sor-ri - so ba - le-nò! In-fe-li-ce! del-la
near, And from her lips a smile broke forth; Ah, her spirit, most un
fp
p
fp
p
f
Tymp.
men-te la vir-tu-de a lei man-cò, a le- - i, a lei, in-fe-
hap-py, Reason's bonds had cast a-way, her spir- - it, un-hap - py! her
Fl. and Cl.
p
fp
li-ce, in-fe-li-ce! del-la men-te la vir-tu-de a lei man-cò! ah!
spir-it most un-hap-py, Reason's bonds, ay, reason's bonds had cast a-way! Ah!
f
Maestoso.
p legato
Oh! qual fu-ne-sto av-ve-ni-men-to!
Oh! dire mis-for-tune, oh day of sor-row,
Chorus.
Maestoso.
Vln. and Tpt.
B. pizz.

tut - ti_ ne in - gom - bra cu - po spa - ven - to! Not - te, ri - co - pri
What gloomy end - ing of_ happy mor - row! Night, cast thy shad - ow
tut - ti_ ne in - gom - bra cu - po spa - ven - to! Not - te, ri - co - pri
What gloomy end - ing of_ happy mor - row! Night, cast thy shad - ow
tut - ti_ ne in - gom - bra cu - po spa - ven - to! Not - te, ri - co - pri
What gloomy end - ing of_ happy mor - row! Night, cast thy shad - ow
la_ ria sventu - ra col te - ne - bro - so tuo den - so vel.
o'er our la - ment - ing, Soon free her spir - it from bonds of earth.
la_ ria sventu - ra col te - ne - bro - so tuo den - so vel.
o'er our la - ment - ing, Soon free her spir - it from bonds of earth.
la_ ria sventu - ra col te - ne - bro - so tuo den - so vel.
o'er our la - ment - ing, Soon free her spir - it from bonds of earth.
Bide-the-Bent.
Ah! quel - la de - stra di san - gue impu - ra l'i - ra non
Oh! heav'n in mer - cy the crime_ for - give her, Sad was her

chia - mi su noi del ciel, Ah! quel - la
fate, cru - el ha - tred's prey, Oh heav'n, in
Ah! quel - la
Oh heav'n, in
Ah! quel - la
Oh heav'n, in
Ah! quel - la
Oh heav'n, in
Tutti.
ff
de - stra di san-gue im-pu - ra l'i - ra non
mer - cy the crime for-give her, sad was her
de - stra di san-gue im-pu - ra l'i - ra non
mer - cy the crime for-give her, sad was her
de - stra di san-gue im-pu - ra l'i - ra non
mer - cy the crime for-give her, sad was her
de - stra di san-gue im-pu - ra l'i - ra non
mer - cy the crime for-give her, sad was her

calando
chia - mi su noi del ciel. El - la in me le lu - ci af-
fate, cru - el ha - tred's prey. Gaz - ing forth with eyes all
chia - mi su noi del ciel.
fate, cru - el ha - tred's prey.
colando
colando
Fl.
Vln.
fis - se, e l'ac - ciar, l'ac-ciar strin - ge - va!
va - cant, in her hand she held the dag - ger.
E l'ac-
In her
Tromboni & Bassi.

Ah!
Ah!
ciar, l'ac-ciar strin - ge - va!
hand she held the dag - ger!
ciar, l'ac-ciar strin - ge - va! l'ac - ciar!
hand she held the dag - ger! Ah me!
ciar, l'ac-ciar strin - ge - va! l'ac - ciar!
hand she held the dag - ger! Ah me!
ff
ah! quel - la de - stra di_ san-gue im-pu - ra
may heav'n in mer - cy the_ crime for-give her,
ff
Ah! quel - la de - stra di_ san-gue im-pu - ra
may heav'n in mer - cy the_ crime for-give her,
ff
Ah! quel - la de - stra di_ san-gue im-pu - ra
may heav'n in mer - cy the_ crime for-give her,
ff
Ah! quel - la de - stra di_ san-gue im-pu - ra
may heav'n in mer - cy the_ crime for-give her,
ff

Più mosso.
f
l'i - ra non chia - mi su noi del ciel, non chia-mi
Sad was her fate, cru - el ha - tred's prey, sad was her
f
l'i - ra non chia - mi su noi del ciel, non chiami
Sad was her fate, cru - el ha - tred's prey, sad was her
pp
l'i - ra non chia - mi su noi del ciel, l'i - ra non chiami su
Sad was her fate, cru - el ha - tred's prey, sad was her fate, cru - el
pp
l'i - ra non chia - mi su noi del ciel, l'i - ra non chiami su
Sad was her fate, cru - el ha - tred's prey, sad was her fate, cru - el
Più mosso.
ff
l'i - ra su no - i del ciel, non chia - mi
fate, cru - el ha - tred's prey, sad was her
l'i - ra su no - i del ciel, non chia - mi
fate, cru - el ha - - tred's prey, sad was her
noi del ciel, l'i - ra non chia - mi su
ha - - tred's prey, sad was her fate, cru - el
noi del ciel, l'i - ra non chia - mi su
ha - - tred's prey, sad was her fate, cru - el

l'i - ra su no - i del ciel, l'i - - ra del
fate, cru - el ha - tred's prey, sad was her

l'i - ra su no - i del ciel, l'i - - ra del
fate, cru - el ha - - tred's prey, sad was her

noi del ciel, l'i - - ra del
ha - - tred's prey, sad was her

noi del ciel, l'i - - ra del
ha - - tred's prey, sad was her

8

ciel, sì, sì, l'i - ra del ciel, sì, sì, l'i - ra del ciel.
fate, ah yes, sad was her fate, ah yes, sad was her fate.

ciel, sì, sì, l'i - ra del ciel, sì, sì, l'i - ra del ciel.
fate, ah yes, sad was her fate, ah yes, sad was her fate.

ciel, sì, sì, l'i - ra del ciel, sì, sì, l'i - ra del ciel.
fate, ah yes, sad was her fate, ah yes, sad was her fate.

ciel, sì, sì, l'i - ra del ciel, sì, sì, l'i - ra del ciel.
fate, ah yes, sad was her fate, ah yes, sad was her fate.

8

Lento.

Lento.

Nº 14. "Alfin son tua.,,

Recitative and Aria.

(Lucy Ashton enters in a plain white dress; her hair dishevelled. She is deathly pale, and out of her senses.)

Bide-the-Bent. Andante.

Ec-co-la!
See she comes!

Chorus.

SOPRANO.

Oh giu-sto cie-lo!
Oh sight of sor-row,

TENOR.

Oh giu-sto cie-lo!
Oh sight of sor-row,

BASS.

Oh giu-sto cie-lo!
Oh sight of sor-row,

Andante.

Strings, Corni, Tromba, & Fag.

Par dal-la tom-ba u-sci-ta!
as from the grave a-ris-en.
Par dal-la tom-ba u-sci-ta!
as from the grave a-ris-en.
Par dal-la tom-ba u-sci-ta!
as from the grave a-ris-en.
Fl.
p
Cl. sustain.
Strings pizz.
Lucy.
Il dol-ce suo-no mi col-pì di sua vo-ce! Ah! quel-la
I hear the breathing of his voice low and ten-der, That voice re-
Cor.
Fag. and Cor.
vo-ce m'è qui nel cor di-sce-sa! Ed-gar-do! io ti son
soundeth with-in my heart for ev-er. Oh Edgar, why were we
p
Strings.
re-sa, Ed-gar-do! ah! Ed-gar-do mi-o! sì, ti son
part-ed? oh Ed-gar, say, why didst thou leave me? Let me not
Fl.
Cl.

affrett.
re - sa; fug-gi-ta io son da' tuoi ne-mi - ci, da' tuoi ne-mi -
mourn thee; see, for thy sake I've all for-sak - en, I've all for-sak -
Ob. Cl. Hn. Bssn.
ci.
en.
Recit.
Un
What
Fl.
p
rall. a tempo
ge-lo mi ser-peg-gia nel sen! tre-ma o gni
shudder do I feel through my veins! My heart is
Recit.
Hn.
Cl.
p
fi - bra! va-cil-la il piè! - Pres-so la fon - te me-co t'as-si-di al-
trembling, my senses fail! Come to the foun-tain, there let us rest to-
fp Hn. and Bssn. sustain.
fp
quan - to, sì, pres-so la fon-te me - co t'as-si - di!
geth - er, Yes, yes, by the fountain thou'lt rest be-side me.

Allegretto.
Fl. and Cl.
Fag.
Allegro vivace.
Ohi-mè! sorge il tre-men-do fan-tas-ma e ne se-pa-ra! Ohi-mè! ohi-mè! Ed-gar-do! Ed-gar-do! ah! il fan-tas-ma!
Ah me! Look where the spec-tre a-ris-es! Stand-ing be-tween us! A-las, a-las, oh Ed-gar, I've lost thee, ah, see, the spec-tre,
Tymp.
Wood and Brass.
f
pp
'Cello
Cl.
f (terrified)
Tymp.

il fan-tas-ma ne se-pa- - - -
see, the spectre, it di-vides
Tutti.
ff
-ra! Qui ri-co-vria-mo,Edgardo, a piè del-
us! Here we will seek for shelter, be-side the
Recit.
Recit.
l'a-ra. Sparsa è di ro-se!
al-tar. Larghetto. 'Tis strewn with roses!
Fl.
pp Ob. Cl. and Fag.
pp
Un' ar-mo-nia ce-le-ste, di', non a-scol-ti?
Hear'st thou the sounds ce-les-tial, Soar-ing be-yond us?
pp
Andante.
Ah! l'in-no suo-na di
Hark! 'tis the hymn for our
Vln.
pp
pp

con forza
noz-ze! Ah, ah, ah!_ l'in-no di
nuptials! Ah! ah, for_ us they are
Fl.
Cl.
noz - ze! Il ri-to per noi s'appre - sta! Oh me fe-li - ce!_
sing-ing, The al-tar for us is deck'd thus! Oh, hap-py morning!
rall.
Ed-gar-do! Ed-gar-do! Oh!
Oh, Ed-gar, my Ed-gar! Oh!
Allegro.
me fe - li - ce! Oh gio-ja_ che si_
bless - ed_ morn - ing! Oh joy un - told, un -
ff
sen-te, oh gio-ja che si sente, e non si di -
fathom'd, With-in my heart be ev-er, be ev-er hid-
f
p

Maestoso.
ce! Ar-don gl'in-
den! The burning
Larghetto.
cen-si tor-no! Ec-co il mi-nistro!
ta-pers, Round us, the guests as-sembled, waiting, I
Flauti.
Splendon le sa-cre fa-ci, splendon in-
see them, the priest is ready!
Cl.
tor-no! Ec-co il mi-nistro! Por-gi-mi la destra! Oh
"With this ring I wed thee!" Oh
a piacere
a tempo
lie-to gior-no! oh lie-to! Al-fin son tu-a,
day of rap-ture, oh rap-ture! At last I'm thine, love,
colla parte
al-fin sei mi-o, a me ti do-na, a
at last thou'rt mine, love, Heav'n smiles up-on us, And
Fl.
Fag. and Cl.

Lucy.
me ti do - na - un - Di - - o.
love's de - lights have won us.
Norman.
Ab - bi in sì
Oh, send her re -
Bide-the-Bent.
Ab - bi in sì
Oh, send her re -
Chorus.
Ab - bi in sì
Oh, send her re -
Ab - bi in sì
Oh, send her re -
Viola and Cl.
Hn. sustain.
p
(opp.)
O - - gni - pia - cer più - gra - to, sì, o - gni pia -
Ah! we're - no more di - vid - ed, no, no more di -
cru - do sta - - to di lei, Si -
lief, kind heav - - en! Poor maid - en,
cru - do sta - - to di lei, Si -
lief, kind heav - - en! Poor maid - en,
cru - do sta - - to di lei, Si -
lief, kind heav - - en! Poor maid - en,
cru - do sta - - to di lei, Si -
lief, kind heav - - en! Poor maid - en,

ce - re mi fia con te di - vi-so, con te, con
vid - ed, 'Tis heav'n to be with thee, with thee, with
gno - re, di lei pie - tà.
true to the faith she vow'd,
gno - re, di lei pie - tà.
true to the faith she vow'd,
Si-gnor, pie -
the faith she
gno - re, di lei pie - tà,
true to the faith she vow'd,
Si-gnor, Si-gnor, pie -
the faith, the faith she
gno - re, di lei pie - tà,
true to the faith she vow'd,
Si-gnor, Si-gnor, pie -
the faith, the faith she
Fl.
te. Del ciel cle - men - te, del
thee, My own for - ev - er, By
tà.
vow'd.
tà.
vow'd.
tà.
vow'd.
col canto
p
Fl.
ciel cle-men - te un ri - so la vi - ta a noi sa -
heav'n to me thou wert guid - ed, And smil-ing be - fore us

rà, la vi - ta a noi, a noi sa -
bright dawns the future, with - out a
rà, del ciel clemente, clemente un ri - so la vi - ta a noi, a noi sa -
cloud, smil-ing before us, smil-ing before us, bright dawns the future, without a -
rà, la vi - ta a noi sa - rà,
cloud, Ah, yes, with-out a cloud,
a noi sa - rà, sa -
ay, smil-ing with-out a -
Norman.
Pie -
She
Bide-the-Bent.
Pie -
She
Chorus.
Pie -
She
Pie -
She

Allegro.
rà.
cloud.
tà!
vow'd!
tà!
vow'd!
tà!
vow'd!
tà!
vow'd!
Allegro.
Tutti.
Bide-the-Bent.
S'a-van-za En-ri-co!
Here comes her broth-er!
Henry. (rushing in.)
Di-te-mi: ve-ra è l'a-tro-ce sce-na?
Is it true; hath she the crime com-mit-ted?
Bide-the-Bent.
Ve-
Ah,

Henry.
ra, pur trop - po!
'tis but too true!
Ah per - fi - da! ne a -
Per - fid - ious girl, may
vrai con - de - gna pe - na!
sor - row fall up - on thee,
(Hastily approaching Lucy.)
Bide-the-Bent.
Oh
Oh
Chorus.
T'ar - re - sta!
Oh leave her—
ciel!— Non ve - di lo sta - to su - o?
heav'n! nor sor - row nor joy can reach her.
Lucy. (in delirium.)
Che
What

Lucy.
chie - di?
would he?
Che chie - di!
What would he?
(gazing on her.)
Henry.
Oh, qual pal - lor!
Oh, why so pale?
Bide-the-Bent.
Ha la ragion smar -
She is bereft of
f
fp
fp
Ah me mi - se - ra!
Ah, un - hap - py me!
Gran Di - o!
Oh, heav - en!
ri - ta. Tre - ma - re, o bar - ba - ro, tu
rea - son. Oh, trem - ble, thou cru - el man, 'tis
f
Lucy.
Meno.
Non mi guardar sì fie - ro, se -
Look not so dark - ly on me, It
Bide-the-Bent.
dêi per la sua vi - ta.
thou to this hast brought her.
Meno
Strings.
p
p
Hn.
Cello.
Bassi.
gnai quel fo - glio, è ve - ro, sì, sì, sì, è ve -
is my writing, why shun me? Why, ah why dost shun
Cl. and Bssn.
Strings.

(as in a vision.)
ro — Nel-l'i - ra sua ter - ri - bi - le cal-pe-sta, oh Dio, l'a - nel - lo! — mi ma-le-di - ce! Ah!
me? Oh say, what mean those wrathful words, Why take the ring thou gav'st me? Why dost thou curse me? Ah,
p
f rall.
Allegro mosso.
vit - ti - ma fui d'un cru-del fra - tel - lo: ma o - gnor, o - gnor, t'a -
know'st thou not I must o - bey my broth - er! My heart is thine for
p Cl.Cor. and Fag.
Strings pizz.
ma - i, o - gno - ra, Ed - gar - do, sì, o - gnor, o-gnor t'a - ma - i, ah! e
ev - er, for ev - er, Oh, Ed - gar, my heart is thine for ev-er, ah, for
8
Fl. Ob.
p
Lucy.
t'a-mo an - cor — Ed - gar - do mi - o, sì, te lo giu - ro, o - gnor t'a -
ev-er I'm thine! Turn to me, Ed - gar, Say thou be-liev'st me, I love thee
Henry.
pp
Ah! di le - i, Si-gnor, pie-tà! Ah sì, di
Heav'n, have pit - y up - on her woe! Oh heav'n, hav
Bide-the-Bent.
Pie - ta di lei,
Oh heav'n, pit - y
8

ma - i e t'a-mo an - cor, o - gnor, o - gnor t'a - ma - i, ah! e
ev - er, I'm ev - er thine, I'm thine, I'm thine for ev - er, Ah, for
le - i, Si-gnor, pie - tà, pie - tà, pie - tà, di lei pie - tà!
pit - y up-on her woe, oh, heav'n, have pit - y on her woe!
Si - gnor, pie - tà, pie - tà!
her woe, pit - y her woe!
pp
t'a - mo an - cor, ah! t'a - mo, t'a - mo an - cor, ah!
ev - er I'm thine, I love thee, ev - er I'm thine, Ah,
ah Si - gnor, pie - tà, Si -
heav'n have pit - y, pit - y
ah Si - gnor, pie - tà, Si -
heav'n have pit - y, pit - y
f
t'a - mo an - cor, t'a - mo, t'a - mo an - cor!
ev - er I'm thine, Ah, for ev - er I'm thine!
gnor, pie - tà, ah pie - tà!
on her woe, on her woe!
gnor, pie - tà, ah pie - tà!
on her woe, on her woe!
f
Cor.

Chi mi no-ma-sti? Ar-
Who stands be-side thee? 'Tis
Bassi and Vln II.
Vln I. pizz.
Viola, Cor. and Fag.
tu-ro! Tu no-ma-sti. Ar-tu-ro!
Ar-thur! Ah, what would he Not Ar-thur!
Tutti.
Ah! non fug-gir! Ah, per pie-tà!
Ah! let me fly Mer-ci-ful heav'n!
Lucy.
no, non fug-gir! ah per-don! ah per-
Oh, let me fly, Ed-gar mine, where art
Henry.
In-fe-li-ce! ah pie-tà, Si
Maid un-happy! Heav'n be-hold and
Bide-the-Bent.
In-fe-li-ce! ah pie-tà, Si
Maid un-happy! Heav'n be-hold and
Chorus.
In-fe-li-ce! ah pie-tà, Si-
Maid un-happy! Heav'n be-hold and
In-fe-li-ce! ah pie-tà, Si-
Maid un-happy! Heav'n be-hold and
In-fe-li-ce! ah pie-tà, Si-
Maid un-happy! Heav'n be-hold and
ff

don, per - don! Ah!
thou, ah, where? Ah!
gnor, pie - tà! Lu - ci - a! Lu - ci - a! gran Di -
end her woe! My sister, my sister! She hears
gnor, pie - tà! Qual not - te di ter - ror
end her woe! Oh, night of grief and of doom,
gnor, pie - tà! Qual not - te di ter - ror, oh
end her woe! Oh, night of grief and of doom, oh,
gnor, pie - tà! Qual not - te di ter - ror,
end her woe! Oh, night of grief and doom,
gnor, pie - tà! Qual not - te di ter - ror,
end her woe! Oh, night of grief and doom,
p cresc. poco a poco
(falling on her knees)
Ah! no, non fug -
Ah! no, leave me
o! Ah Lu - ci - a!
not, oh what sor - row!
di ter - ror, di ter - ror!
night of grief and of doom!
not - te di ter - ror!
night of grief and doom!
di ter - ror, di ter - ror!
night of grief and of doom!
di ter - ror, di ter - ror!
night of grief and of doom!
Vlns.
col canto
pp
Viola.

Moderato.
gir, Ed-gar-do!
not, oh Ed-gar!
Wood.
p
Strings pizz.
Cor
Tymp.
Cor. and Fag.
rall.
Lucy.
Spar-gi d'a-ma-ro pian-to il mio ter-re-stre ve-lo, men-tre las-sù nel cie-lo io pre-ghe-rò, pre-ghe-rò per te.
Cast on my grave a flow-er, But let there be no weep-ing, When 'neath the turf I'm sleep-ing, Let not an eye, not an eye grow dim,
Strings
Cl.
Fl.
Cor. and Fag.
rall. e portando la voce
Al giunger tu-o sol-tan-to
For 'mid the fields of a-zure,
Fl. and Cl.
8

stringendo
fia bel-lo il ciel per me! ah sì, ah sì, ah sì, per
I go to wait for him, ah yes, ah yes, ah yes, I
string. e cresc.
a tempo
string.
me, fia bel-lo il ciel, il ciel per me, ah sì, ah
wait, 'mid fields of a-zure I wait for him, ah yes, ah
Tutti.
Fl. and Cl.
fa tempo
string. e cresc.
sì, ah sì, per me,
yes, ah yes, I wait,
Fl. Ob. Cl.
sì, per me,
I wait,
Fl.
Cl.
per me, per
I wait for
opp.

Più mosso.
Lucy.
me.
him.
Henry.
Gior - ni d'a - ma - ro pian - - to
Oh grief be - yond all mea - - sure,
Bide-the-Bent.
Più raf - fre - na - re il pian - - to
Short were thy days of plea - - sure,
Chorus.
TENOR.
Più raf - fre - na - re il
Short were thy days of
BASS.
Più raf - fre - na - re il
Short were thy days of
Più mosso.
Henry.
ser - ba il ri - mor - so a me, sì,
Oh most un - hap - py day,
Bide-the-Bent.
pos - si - bi - le non è,
Grief stole thy life a - way,
Ah, più raf - fre - na - re il
Ah, short were thy young days of
pian - - to pos - si - bi - le non
plea - - sure, Grief stole thy life a -
pian - - to pos - si - bi - le non
plea - - sure, Grief stole thy life a -

ser - - ba il ri - mor - so a me,
Oh most un - hap - py day,

pos - si bi - le non è,
grief stole thy life a - way,

pian - to pos - si - bi - le non è,
plea - sure, grief stole thy life a - way,

è, no, no, pos - si - bi - le non è,
way, ah yes, grief stole thy life a - way,

è, pos - si - bi - le non è,
way, grief stole thy life a - way,

f

Lucy.

Ah!
Ah!

ah sì, a me.
un - hap - py day.

ah no, non e.
un - hap - py day.

ah no, non è.
un - hap - py day.

ah no, non è.
un - hap - py day.

ah no, non è.
un - hap - py day.

Spar - gi d'a - ma - ro pian - to il mio ter - re - stre
Cast on my grave a flow - er, But let there be no
ve - - - lo, men - tre las - sù nel
weep - - - ing, When 'neath the turf I'm
rall. e portando la voce
cie - - lo io pre-ghe-rò, pre-ghe - rò per te; Al giun-ger
sleep - - ing, Let not an eye, not an eye grow dim; For 'mid the
tu - o sol - tan - - to fia bel-lo il ciel per
fields of a - - zure, I go to wait for
string.
a tempo
me! ah sì, ah sì, ah sì, per - me,
him, ah yes, ah yes, ah yes, ah yes,
string. e cresc.
f a tempo

p
fia_ bel - lo il ciel, il ciel per me, ah
'Mid fields of a - zure I wait for him, ah
p
string
sì, ah sì, ah sì, per me,
yes, ah yes, ah yes, I wait,
string. e cresc.
p
sì,
pp
per me, per
I wait, I
me, per
wait for
opp.

Più Allegro.
Lucy.
me. Ah ch'io
him. Yes, in
Henry.
Ah, vi - ta d'a - ma - -ro, d'a - ma - ro
Oh, grief be - yond mea- -sure, grief be - yond
Bide-the-Bent.
Ah, più raf - fre - na- -re il
Ah, short were thy days of
Chorus.
Ah, più raf - fre - na- - - re il
Ah, short were thy days of
Ah, più raf - fre - na- -re il
Ah, short were thy days of
Ah, più raf - fre - na- -re il
Ah, short were thy days of
Più Allegro.
spi- -ri ac - can- - -to a
heav- -en. I go to
pian- -to ser - ba il ri - mor- - -so a
mea- -sure, Oh, most un - hap- - -py
pian- -to no, no, pos - si- -bi le non
plea- -sure, Ah, yes, grief stole thy life a -
pian- -to no, no, pos - si- -bi - le non
plea- -sure, Ah, yes, grief stole thy life a -
pian- -to no, no, pos - si- -bi - le non
plea- -sure, Ah, yes, grief stole thy life a -
pian- -to no, no, pos - si- -bi - le non
plea- -sure, Ah, yes, grief stole thy life a -

te, ac - - can - - to a te!
wait for him I love,
me, il ri - mor - so a me,
day, most un - hap - - - py day,
è, no, no, non e,
way, thy life a - - way,
Ah ch'io spi - ri
Yes, in hea - ven,
vi - ta d'a - ma - ro, d'a - ma - ro pian - to
Grief be - yond mea - sure, grief be - yond mea - sure,
più raf - fre - na - - re il pian - to
Short were thy days of plea - sure,
f

ac - can - - to a te, ac - -
I go to wait for
ser - ba il ri - mor - - so a me, sì,
oh, most un - hap - - py day, un - -
no, no, pos - si - bi - le non è, no,
ah, yes, grief stole thy life a - way, thy
no, no, pos - si - bi - le non è, no,
ah, yes, grief stole thy life a - way, thy
no, no, pos - si - bi - le non è, no,
ah, yes, grief stole thy life a - way, thy
no, no, pos - si - bi - le non è, no,
ah, yes, grief stole thy life a - way, thy
can - - to a te, ap - - pres - so
him I love, for him
sì, a me, sì, sì,
hap - - py day, un - - hap -
no, non è, no, no,
life a - - way, grief stole
no, non è, no, no,
life a - - way, grief stole
no, non è, no, no,
life a - - way, grief stole
no, non è, no, no,
life a - - way, grief stole

a te, ap - pres - so a
I love, for him, for him
a me, sì, sì, a
py day, un - hap - py
non è, no, no, non
thy life, thy life a -
non è, no, no, non
thy life, thy life a -
non è, no, no, non
thy life, thy life a -
non è, no, no, non
thy life, thy life a -
f
te, a
I
f
me, a
day, ah
f
è, no, non
way, yes, a -
f
è, no, non
way yes, a -
f
è, no, non
way yes, a -
f
è, no, non
way, yes, a -
f

(falls swooning into Alice's arms.)
te!
love!
me!
me!
è!
way!
è!
way!
è!
way!
è!
way!
ff

Nº 15. "Si tragga altrove.,,

Recit.

Norman.
ca-sa infe-li-ce, hai tu de-sta-ta la pri-mie-ra scin-til-la! Io non cre-
joice in thy do-ing. Thou vile in-former, 'twas thro' thee all was known. I ne'er in-
ff
Bide-the-Bent.
de-i_ Tu del ver-sa-to san-gue, em-pio, tu se-i la ria ca-
tend-ed_ Thou of this grief art guilty, trai-tor, the grief and guilt we de-
gion! Quel san-gue al ciel t'ac-cu-sa, e già la man su-
plore! The ven-geance of heav'n be on thee, yet ere chas-tise-ment
f
pre-ma se-gna la sua sen-ten-za! Or vanne, e tre-
reach thee, I bid thee quit my pres-ence, for ev-er, or trem-
(Bide-the-Bent follows Lucy; exit Norman at the opposite side)
ma!
ble!
pp

Nº 16. "Fra poco a me ricovero.,,"

Final Aria.

A place outside the Castle of Wolf's-crag; there is a practicable gateway. An illuminated hall seen in the distance. Tombs of the Ravenswoods. Night.

Edgar.
Tom - be de-gl'a-vi
Tomb of my sainted
Recit.
mie - i, l'ul - ti - mo a - van-zo d'u-na stirpe infe - li - ce, deh! rac - co - glie - te
fa - thers, o - pen your por-tals; I, the last of my kin-dred, am come to rest be -
vo - i.
side them.
a tempo
ff
p
Cessò del - l'i - ra il bre - ve
The flame of an-ger hath spent its
Recit.
fo - co; sul ne - mi - co ac - cia - ro ab - ban - do - nar mi
fu - ry, for my wea - ry spir - it the grave a - lone hath
p
Larghetto.
vo'. Per me la vi - ta è or - ren - do
peace. Why should I lin - ger, naught, naught is
Strings.
p

pe - so! l'u - ni - ver - so in-te - ro è un de-
left me, With - out her this world is but a
Fl.
Cl.
Cor. sustain
ser - to per me - sen - za Lu - ci - a! Di
des - ert, a des - ert, black and lone-ly! I
Allegro.
fa-ci tut-ta-vi-a splen-de il ca-stel-lo Ah! scarsa fu la not-te al tri-
see the castle gleaming with fes-tive torch-es; Ah! gladness and rejoic-ing sur-
f
pu - dio! In-gra-ta don-na! men-tr'io mi strug-go
round thee! Un-grate-ful maid-en! While I, de-spair-ing,
in di-spe-ra-to pian-to, tu ri-di, e-sul-ti a can-to al fe-li - ce con-
mourn that my hopes have per-ished, be - side thy chosen con-sort thou art beaming with

Larghetto.
sor-te! Tu del-le gio-je in se-no, tu del-le gio-je in
pleasure! Thou full of hope and gladness, thou full of hope and
opp.
io del-la mor- te!
I die de spair- ing!
se-no, io del-la mor- - te!
gladness, I die de-spair - - ing!
Ob.
Fag.
Larghetto.
Cor.
p
Fag.
Tromba and Tymp.
Fra
To
po-co a me ri- co-ve-ro da-rà ne-glet-to a-vel-lo,
earth I bid a last fare-well, The tomb will soon close o'er me,
Cor. and Fag.
u-na pie-to-sa la-gri-ma non scende-ra su quel - lo! ah!
Friend-less, un-wept and un-be-lov'd, No ray of hope be-fore me, ah!
Viole and 'Cello.

rit.

fin de-gli e-stin-ti, ahi mi-se-ro! — man-ca il con-for-to a

Tears, that are balm for mis-e-ry, — Ne'er will be shed for

fp *rit.*

a tempo

me. Tu pur, tu pur di-men-ti-ca quel

me. For-get, for-get a heart be-tray'd, For-

Viol. II. Viol. I.

a tempo

mar-mo di-spre-gia-to:

get the grave that hides — me,

Mai non pas-sar-vi, o bar-ba-ra, del

But ne'er, thou false one, near it stray, With

— tuo con-sor-te a la-to. Ah! ri-spet-ta al-men le

— him whose joy de-rides me. Ah! nor vex the spir-it's

ce - ne-ri di chi mo-ria per te, ri-spetta almen le
last re-pose of him who died for thee, vex not the spirit's
rit.
ce - ne - ri _ di chi mo-ria per te! Mai non pas -
last _ re - pose of him who died for thee. Ah _ yes, for -
Poco più
p col canto
Poco più
fp
cresc.
con calore
rit.
sar - vi, tu _ lo di - men - ti - ca, ri - spet-ta al-me - no chi muore per
get me, for - get a _ heart betray'd, thou false one, vex ___ not my last _ re -
cresc.
col canto
fp
fp
a tempo
te, mai non pas - sar - vi, tu _ lo di - men - ti - ca, ri - spet-ta al -
pose, Ah yes, for - get me, for - get a _ heart betray'd, but oh, thou
fp
fp
fp
fp
me - no _ chi _ muo - re, chi muo - re per te, o
false _ one, _ oh _ vex not my spir-it's last re - pose, oh
Corni
p
p

bar - ba - ra, io mo - ro per te!
faith - less maid, I die for thee!
Moderato.
Chorus.
TENOR. (Coming from the Castle)
BASS.
Oh me - schi - na!
Oh what sor - row!
Oh me - schi - na!
Oh what sor - row!
Moderato.
Cl.
Brass
Stings and Timp.
Oh fa - to or - ren - do! più spe - rar non gio - va o -
Our hopes are end - ed! Death in mer - cy soon re -
Oh fa - to or - ren - do! più spe - rar non gio - va o -
Our hopes are end - ed! Death in mer - cy soon re -
ma - i, o - ma - i!
lease her, re - lease her!
ma - i, o - ma - i!
lease her, re - lease her!

ve -
mourn-ing
Que-sto dì che sta sor - gen - do tra-mon - tar più non ve -
Ah, this day that dawn'd in glad - ness, Must in tears and mourning
Que-sto dì che sta sor - gen - do tra-mon - tar più non ve -
Ah, this day that dawn'd in glad - ness, Must in tears and mourning
p
Edgar.
drà! Giusto cie-lo! rispon - de-te, ri-spon-de - te ah!
close! Why la-ment ye! tell, oh tell me, why lament ye? ah!
drà!
close!
Oh me-
Oh what
drà!
close!
Oh me-
Oh what
ff
Di chi mai, di chi pian -
Say for whom, for whom ye
schi - - - - na!
sor - - - - row!
schi - - - - na!
sor - - - - row!
ge - - te? ri-spon - de-te, ri-spon-de-te per pie -
sor - - - row? Ah, in pit-y, ah, in pit-y tell me

(terror-stricken)

tà! Lu-cia di-ces-te! Su par-la-te.
all. Ah, what of Lu-cy! what, oh tell me,

Di Lu-ci-a. La meschi-na_ Sì; la mi-se-ra sen
'Tis for Lu-cy, hapless maiden, hap-less maiden, she is

Di Lu-ci-a. La meschi-na_ Sì; la mi-se-ra sen
'Tis for Lu-cy, hapless maiden, hap-less maiden, she is

p *affrett. un poco*

Moderato.

Ah!_
Ah!_

muo-re. Fur le noz-ze a lei fu-ne-ste, di ra-
dy-ing, Since the hour of her es-pous-al, Heav'n of

muo-re. Fur le noz-ze a lei fu-ne-ste, di ra-
dy-ing, Since the hour of her es-pous-al, Heav'n of

Moderato.

Vln. I.
Cl.
p
Cor. Fag. & Strings pizz.

gion la tras-se a-mo-re, s'av-vi-ci-na al-l'o-re e-stre-me, e te
rea-son hath be-reft_her, Ev-'ry pulse of life hath left_her, With her

p

gion la tras-se a-mo-re, s'av-vi-ci-na al-l'o-re e-stre-me, e te
rea-son hath be-reft_her, Ev-'ry pulse of life hath left_her, With her

Edgar.
Ah, Lu - ci - - a!
Ah! I wrong'd her!
Que - sto dì che sta sor -
Ah, this day that dawn'd in
chie - de, per te ge - me
dy - ing breath she calls thee
Que - sto dì che sta sor -
Ah, this day that dawn'd in
chie - de, per te ge - me
dy - ing breath she calls thee
Que - sto dì che sta sor -
Ah, this day that dawn'd in
Tutti.
muo - re! Lu - ci - - a! ah!
dy - ing! be - loved one, ah!
gen - do tra - mon - tar più non ve - drà!
glad - ness Must in tears and mourn - ing close!
gen - do tra - mon - tar più non ve - drà! di ra -
glad - ness Must in tears and mourning close! Heav'n of
gen - do tra - mon - tar più non ve - drà! di ra -
glad - ness Must in tears and mourning close! Heav'n of
f
Edgar.
Que - sto
Ah, this
gion la tras - se a - mo - re, e te chie - de, per te ge - me
rea - son hath be - reft her, With her dy - ing breath she calls thee.
gion la tras - se a - mo - re, e te chie - de, per te ge - me
rea - son hath be - reft her, With her dy - ing breath she calls thee.
p

dì che sta sor-gen-do tra-mon-tar più non ve-drà la mia Lu-ci-a?
day that dawn'd in gladness Must in tears and mourning close, a-las! I wrong'd her!
Chorus.
Di ra-
Heav'n of
Di ra-
Heav'n of
f
pp
f
gion la tras-se a-mo-re, per te, sì, sì, per
rea-son hath be-reft her, on thee, on thee she
gion la tras-se a-mo-re, per te, sì, sì, per
rea-son hath be-reft her, on thee, on thee she
Meno Allegro.
Ah!
Ah!
p
te. Rim-bom-ba già la squil-la in suon di mor-te.
calls. Oh, hark, the deathbell tolls for one de-part-ing.
p
te. Rim-bom-ba già la squil-la in suon di mor-te.
calls. Oh, hark, the deathbell tolls for one de-part-ing.
(Bell.)
f
Meno Allegro.
lento
p
(Bell.)
f
f

Allegro vivace.
Quel suo-no in cor mi piom - ba!
It is my knell 'tis sound - ing.
Allegro vivace.
Vln. and 'Cello.
Fag.
È de-ci-sa la mia sor-te!
Naught shall lon-ger now re - strain me,
Ri-ve-der-la ancor vo -
once a-gain I will be -
(detaining him)
Oh Di - o!
What wouldst thou?
Oh Di - o!
What wouldst thou?
cresc.
gl'i-o,
hold her—
ri - ve - der - la e
I will see her, un -
Qual tra - spor - to, scon - si - glia - to! ah de - si-sti, ah rie - di in
Calm, oh calm thee, it were mad-ness, oh, we pray thee, change thy
Qual tra - spor - to, scon - si - glia - to! ah de - si-sti, ah rie - di in
Calm, oh calm thee, it were mad-ness, oh, we pray thee, change thy
sempre cresc.

(rushing off)
po - - scia
hand me
te, in te.
rash re - - solve.
te, in te.
rash re - - solve.
Bide-the-Bent.
Do - ve cor - - ri, sven - - tu - ra - to?
Whith - er dost thou bend thy foot-steps?
El - la in ter - ra più non è.
She on earth has ceased to be.
Edgar.
Lu - ci - a!
What say'st thou?
Bide-the-Bent.
Sven - tu - ra - to!
Yes, thou'st lost her!

Edgar.
a piacere
In ter - ra più non e? el - la
Ah no, those words un - say. Speak, where
Bide-the-Bent.
Edgar.
Meno
dunque_ È in cie - lo. Lu - ci - a più non è!
is she? In heav - en. My Lu - cy is no more!
f
Meno
Strings
Chorus.
Sven-tu - ra - to!
Oh what sor - row!
Sven-tu - ra - to!
Oh what sor - row!
Sven-tu - ra - to!
Oh what sor - row!
Sven-tu - ra - to!
Oh what sor - row!
Cor. and Fag.
Moderato.
Fl.
Cl.
8
Ob. etc.
Strings pizz.
p
Cor. Fag.

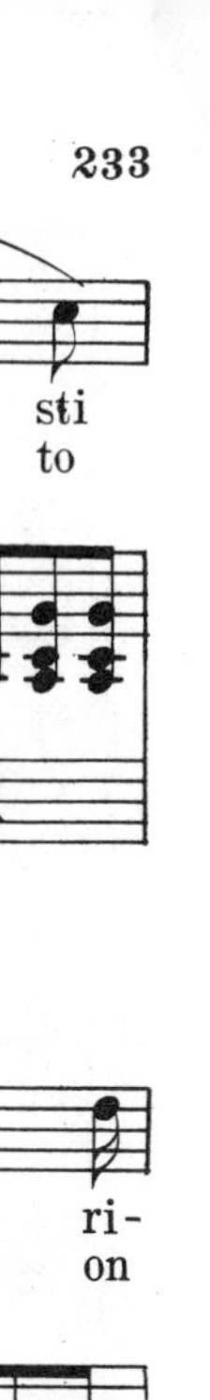
Edgar. (rousing himself.)
p
Tu che a Dio spie - ga - sti
Thou hast spread thy wings to
rall.
p

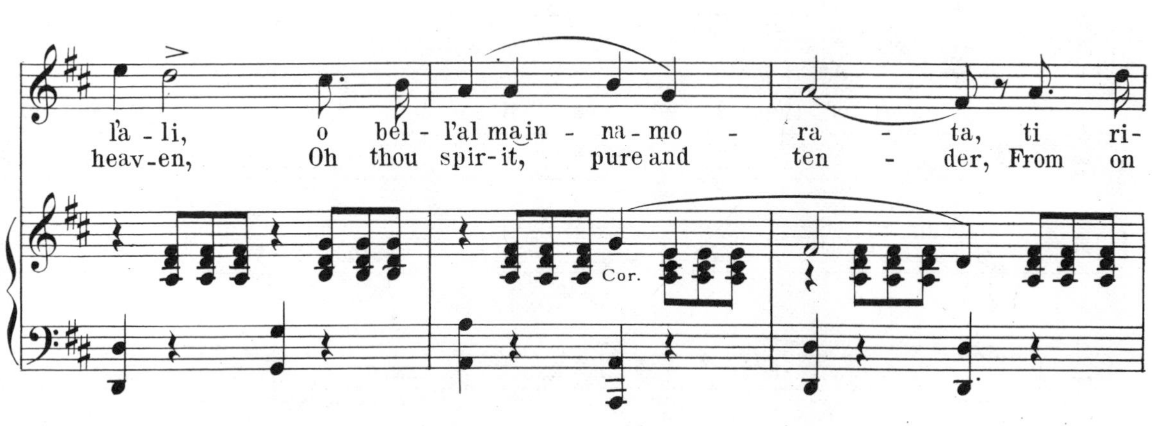
l'a - li, o bel - l'al ma in - na - mo - ra - ta, ti ri -
heav-en, Oh thou spir - it, pure and ten - der, From on
Cor.

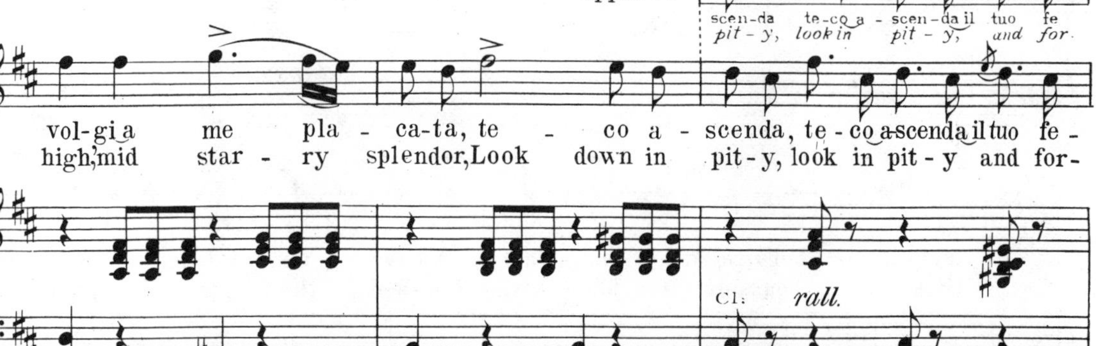
oppure.
scen-da te-co a - scen-da il tuo fe
pit - y, look in pit - y, and for-
vol - gi a me pla - ca - ta, te - co a - scenda, te - co a scenda il tuo fe -
high, 'mid star - ry splendor, Look down in pit - y, look in pit - y and for -
Cl. rall.

del. Ah! se l'i - ra dei mor - ta - li fe - ce a noi sì cru - da
give. Tho' by mor - tals doom'd to sev - er, Ours a love that can - not
Ob.
a tempo
Cl. & 'Cello.

guer - ra, se di - vi - si fum - mo in ter - ra, ne con -
per - ish, Thee on earth a - lone I cher - ish, Reft of
Fl. Ob.
Poco più mosso.
giun - ga il Nu - me in ciel, o bel - l'al - ma in - na - mo -
thee, reft of thee I will not live, no, thou spir - it pure and
Cl. sustain.
calando
ra - ta, bel - l'al - ma in - na - mo - ra - ta, ne con - giun - ga il Nu - me in
ten - der, thou spir - it pure and ten - der, reft of thee, I will not
Cor. & Fag. sustain.
calando
p cresc.
ciel, o bel - l'al - ma in - na - mo - ra - ta, bel - l'al - ma in - na - mo -
live, no, thou spir - it pure and ten - der, thou spir - it pure and
rinf.
Allegro.
ra - ta, ne con - giun - ga il Nu - me in ciel! Io ti
ten - der, reft of thee, reft of thee, I'll not live. Thee I
Cl. Fl.
Cello
Vln. & Fag.
p

Bide-the-Bent.
se-guo_ For-sen-na-to! for-sen-na-to! Ah! che fa-i? ah! che
fol-low. Tempt not heav-en with thy rash-ness, Ah, thy mad-ness heav'n will
Chorus.
Ah! che fa-i? ah! che
Ah! thy mad-ness heav'n will
Ah! che fa-i? ah! che
Ah! thy mad-ness heav'n will
cresc.
Edgar.
Bide-the-Bent.
fa-i? Mo-rir vo-glio, mo-rir vo-glio. Ri-tor-na in
pun-ish! Life is hate-ful where she is not! Oh, calm thy
fa-i?
pun-ish!
Ri-tor-na in
Oh, calm thy
fa-i?
pun-ish!
Ri-tor-na in
Oh, calm thy
Fl. Ob. etc.
f
Edgar (stabs himself)
Bide-the-Bent.
te, ri-tor-na in te, ri-tor-na in te. No, no, no! Ah!
grief, 'Twas heaven's de-cree, 'twas heaven's de-cree. No more, no,_ Ah!
te, ri-tor-na in te, ri-tor-na in te.
grief, 'Twas heav-en's de-cree, 'twas heaven's de-cree.
Ah!
Ah!
te, ri-tor-na in te, ri-tor-na in te.
grief, 'Twas heav-en's de-cree, 'twas heaven's de-cree.
Ah!
Ah!
ff
14047

Edgar (with broken voice)
Moderato. Larghetto.
A te ven-go o bel-
None shall part us Oh, be-
Che fa-ce-sti!
Fa-tal rashness!
Cello
Cor.
l'al-ma, ti ri-vol-gi, ah! al tuo fe-
lov'd one, Look in pit-y, ah, look and for-
Scia-gu-ra-to!
Day of sorrow!
del. Ah se l'i-ra dei mor-ta-li
give. Though by mor-tals doom'd to sev-er,
Pen-sa al ciel.
Turn to heav'n.
Chorus.
Qua-le orror! Qua-le orror!
Day of woe! Day of woe!
Cello and Ob.
Cello and Cl.

sì cru - da guer - ra, o bel-
love can - not per - ish, Reft of
Oh Dio, per do - na,
Oh heav'n for - give thee,
ravvivando il tempo
l'al-ma, ne con-giunga il Nu-me in ciel, o bel-l'alma inna-mo-
thee, of thee, I can-not, I can - not live, oh, thou spirit pure and
Pen-sa al ciel.
Turn to heav'n.
Oh tre -
Heav'n - ly
Oh tre -
Heav'n - ly
ravvivando il tempo
ra - ta, bel - l'al -ma in-na - mo - ra - ta, ne con-giun-ga il Nu-me in
ten-der, thou spir-it pure and ten-der, Reft of thee, I will not
Pen - sa al
Oh for -
men - do, oh ne - ro
mer - cy, oh for -
men - do, oh ne - ro
mer - cy, oh for -

cresc.
ciel, o bel - l'al-ma in - na - mo - ra - ta, bel - l'al-ma in - na - mo -
live, oh, thou spir - it pure and ten - der, thou spir - it pure and
ciel, al ciel, al
give, for - - give, for - -
fa - - to! Dio, per - -
give, for - - give, for - -
fa - - to! Dio, per - -
give, for - - give, for - -
cresc.
ra - ta, ne con - giun - ga il Nu - me in ciel! Se di -
ten - der, reft of thee, reft of thee, I'll not live! Though by
ciel, ah scia - gu - ra - to, pensa al ciel. Di - o,
give, Thou heav'n-ly mercy, oh for-give, heav - en,
do - na tan - to or - ror. Di - o,
give, the crime for - give, heav - en,
do - na tan - to or - ror. Di - o,
give, the crime for - give, heav - en,
p

vi - si fummo in ter - ra ne con - giun - ga il Nu - me in ciel, ne con - giun - ga il
mor - tals doom'd to sev - er, Reft of thee, be-reft of thee, 'reft of thee, I no
per - do - na, per - do - na tan - to or - ror,
for - give him, in mer - cy, do thou for - give,
per - do - na, per - do - na tan - to or - ror,
for - give him, in mer - cy, oh, for - give,
per - do - na, per - do - na tan - to or - ror,
for - give him, in mer - cy, do thou for - give,
cresc.
f
Poco più.
Nu - me in ciel, il Nu - me in
more will live, no more I'll
tan - to or - ror, per don,
oh, for - give, for - give;
tan - to or - ror, per - don,
oh, for - give, for - give;
tan - to or - ror, per - don,
oh, for - give, for - give;
ff
f Poco più.

14047

End of the Opera.